Flexibility
Principles & Practice

Christopher M. Norris

Flexibility
Principles & Practice

———

Christopher M. Norris

MSc CBA MCSP SRP

A & C Black · London

First published **1994** by
A & C Black (Publishers) Ltd
35 Bedford Row, London WC1R 4JH

Reprinted 1995

ISBN 0 7136 4037 5

A CIP catalogue record for this book is available from the British Library.

Distributed in the USA by The Talman Company
131 Spring Street, New York, NY10012.

Acknowledgements

Front and back cover photographs by Mike Ellis. All other photographs by Sylvio Dokov. Illustrations by Ron Dixon of 1-11 Line-art. The publishers would like to thank Crystal Palace National Sports Centre and the National Sports Medicine Institute for the use of their facilities, and Puma UK Limited for their contribution.

Thanks also to Rose Macdonald, Brian Stoddart, Linda Smith, Dave Williams, Ayo Falola and Helen Garrett.

Typeset in 11 on 12½ pt Melior by
J&L Composition Ltd, Filey, North Yorkshire
Printed by Bell and Bain Ltd, Glasgow

Contents

Note   Throughout this book individuals are referred to as 'he'. This should, of course, be taken to mean 'he or she' where appropriate.

PART ONE

The Scientific Principles of Flexibility Training

CHAPTER 1

Biomechanical factors in stretching

The study of the effect of mechanical forces on biological materials is known as *biomechanics*. Biomechanical principles are important to all aspects of sports training, but especially to stretching. To be effective, and to prevent injury, stretching exercises must be applied on a foundation of good biomechanical principles.

Leverage

The limbs and spine act as *levers* when we move. A lever is simply a rigid bar which moves around a fixed point called the *pivot* or *fulcrum*. Two forces act on the lever, *effort* and *resistance*. The effort tries to move the lever, while the resistance tries to stop movement. In the body, the effort is supplied by muscle contraction, while the resistance is weight. The weight is a combination of the weight of the moving limb and the weight of any object lifted. Take as an example the arm lifting from the side of the body (*see* fig. 1). The fulcrum is the shoulder joint, the effort is supplied by the deltoid muscle which contracts and abducts the arm, and the resistance is the weight of the arm.

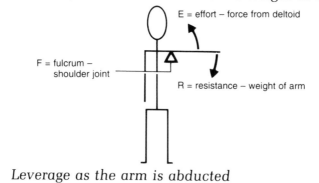

Fig. 1   *Leverage as the arm is abducted*

3

The amount of leverage produced in any exercise can be calculated by multiplying the horizontal distance between the point where the resistance or effort acts and the fulcrum. Figure 2 illustrates a simple example of a lever. A resistance of 6 kg is placed 3 m away from the fulcrum. Multiplying these together gives a leverage force of 18 units. To balance this out, the effort has to be of the same magnitude. So, the 9 kg weight has only to be placed 2 m from the fulcrum for the lever to balance.

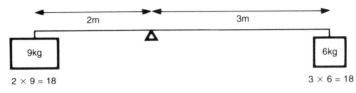

Fig. 2   *Calculating leverage*

It is important to note that the horizontal distance between the fulcrum and effort or resistance is used, rather than simply the distance along the lever. This means that leverage will be greater as a body-part is moved into a horizontal position, and will reduce as the body-part moves away from the horizontal (*see* fig. 3). This fact must always be borne in mind when choosing

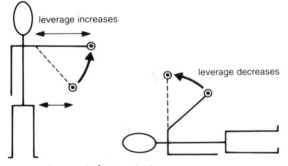

Fig. 3   *Leverage in weight training*

starting positions for stretching exercises, especially with regard to injury to the spine. Take as an example a simple toe-touching movement. Performed from long sitting, the leverage on the spine is minimal (*see* fig. 4(a)); however, the same body movement performed from standing (*see* fig. 4(b)) places a considerable stress on the spine through leverage forces acting on the lumbar region.

This example illustrates an important safety factor with regard to leverage. Exercises which involve moving the spine into a horizontal position will place great amounts of leverage on the

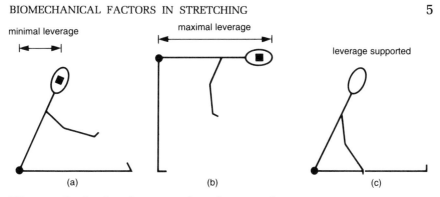

Fig. 4   *Reducing leverage by altering the starting position*

spine and should be used with caution. Often, simply altering the starting position will move the spine away from the horizontal and so reduce the stress on the low back. Where a horizontal position must be used, the spine should be supported. In the examples above, the athlete is stretching the hamstrings by bending forwards. This action places an excessive leverage stress on the spine. Simply by putting one hand down on the knee, the spine is supported and the stress reduced (*see* fig. 4(c)).

Considering the effect of gravity is also important. In figure 5 the athlete is performing the splits. The leverage on the leg is excessive, tending to force the knee downwards and open the joint. This action can severely stress the medial ligament on the inside of the knee. Performing a similar action sitting down takes the weight away from the knee and, although the lever length is the same, the effect on the knee ligaments is considerably reduced, making the exercise far safer.

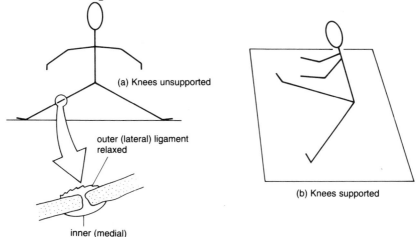

Fig. 5   *Leverage and the splits*

Centre of gravity and stability

The *centre of gravity* of an object is its balance point, where all the weight of the object is focused. The centre of gravity of a symmetrical object, such as a brick, will be at its centre. However, in the case of asymmetrical objects such as the human body, the centre of gravity will be nearer to the larger, and heavier, end.

Because the legs are heavier than the arms, when a person is standing their centre of gravity is not in the middle of the body at the naval, but lower down within the sacrum. As the body moves away from the standard upright position, the centre of gravity also moves. Lifting the arms overhead, for example, moves the centre of gravity upwards; while carrying something moves the centre of gravity towards the object being carried. In addition to the centre of gravity of the body as a whole, each limb also has a centre of gravity. For example, the weight of the arm will act through its own centre of gravity which, rather than being in the middle of the arm at the elbow, is actually closer to the shoulder because the upper arm is heavier than the forearm.

Extending the centre of gravity downwards towards the floor gives us the object's *line of gravity*. Where the centre of gravity was the balance point of an object, the line of gravity can be imagined as a plumb-line hanging down from this point. For an object to remain in balance, its line of gravity must pass through its base of support. If the line of gravity moves outside the base of support, the object becomes unstable and will topple over. To compensate for this, the body position will change when something is carried. In figure 6(a) the centre of gravity of the body is

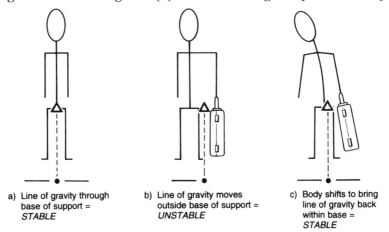

a) Line of gravity through base of support = STABLE

b) Line of gravity moves outside base of support = UNSTABLE

c) Body shifts to bring line of gravity back within base = STABLE

Fig. 6   *The centre of gravity of the body moves when an object is carried*

within the sacrum. In figure 6(b), the suitcase carried in the right hand moves the centre of gravity of the body and case combined to the right. This would move the line of gravity outside the person's base of support, making him unstable. To compensate for this the body position is changed, by leaning over to the left, to pull the line of gravity back within the base of support (*see* fig. 6(c)).

Stability is an important safety factor when performing stretching exercises. An unstable position can cause an athlete to wobble or fall, unintentionally increasing a stretch and pulling muscles or spraining joints. When discussing stability, there are two factors to consider: first, the position of the object's centre of gravity; and second, the size of the object's supporting base.

A lower centre of gravity and a wider base of support will make an object more stable. In addition, the degree of stability is proportional to the distance from the line of gravity to the outer limits of the base of support. Take as an example a motorbike (*see* fig. 7(a)). It has narrow wheels and thus a small base of support. In addition, the rider sits on the machine and so his centre of gravity is high. If the rider were to lean over when going round a bend, he would become less stable (*see* fig. 7(b)). His base of support is the same, and his height above the ground is roughly the same, but his line of gravity has now moved closer to the edge of his base of support. The motorcycle-rider's position is much less stable than that of a racing-car driver: the car has a wide base of support (*see* fig. 7(c)) and, because the driver sits low in the car rather than on top of it, the centre of gravity is lower.

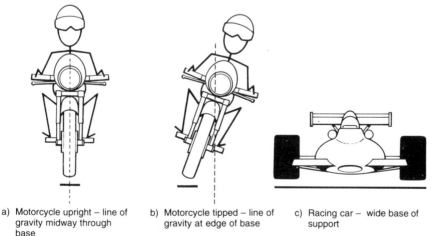

a) Motorcycle upright – line of gravity midway through base

b) Motorcycle tipped – line of gravity at edge of base

c) Racing car – wide base of support

Fig. 7   Stability, centre of gravity and base of support

These same principles can be applied to the exercise situation. When performing standing exercises the centre of gravity is fairly high, so the feet should be apart to widen the base of support and thus make the position more stable. In addition, bending the knees will lower the centre of gravity and further increase stability. When moving, the base of support should be widened in the direction of the movement. Thus when swinging the arms forwards and backwards a wide stance should be taken, with one foot in front of the other, and when moving the arms from side to side the feet should be astride.

Momentum, inertia and friction

Inertia is an object's resistance to change in motion, and is proportional to its weight or 'mass'. Inertia is the force which makes a car hard to push, but a bicycle easy. The heavier an object is, the more inertia it will have. Once inertia has been overcome and the object has begun to move, less force is required to keep it in motion. This is why a heavy object may need a 'good push' to get it moving, and then as it starts to move it does so with a sudden jolt and seems to 'run away with itself'.

Friction, on the other hand, is the force which tries to stop one object from sliding over another. Frictional forces are the result of roughness on the surfaces of two opposing objects, and can be reduced with the use of a lubricant like oil or water. On a rubberised floor the roughness of the floor and the sole of the shoe produces a large amount of friction and gives considerable grip. A shiny wooden floor produces less friction, and a patch of water will reduce friction still further and may cause a person to slip and fall.

Momentum is the combination of how heavy an object is and how quickly it is moving (mass and velocity). A heavy object, such as a leg or the trunk, which is moving quickly will possess a lot of momentum and will be very difficult to stop. The high degree of momentum can take over the movement so that the athlete is no longer able to control it: this is when injuries can occur. To reduce the likelihood of injury through momentum, rapid actions should only be performed in mid-range. When going to full range, actions should be slow and controlled to avoid damage to the joint structures and to muscles. Momentum is a particularly important factor in ballistic stretching (*see* page 53).

Tension, compression and shear

Tension, compression and *shear* are all examples of mechanical stresses which can act on the body, causing the body tissues to deform. Tension is a pulling force. When the spine is flexed, the spinal ligaments are tightened and subjected to a tension stress which causes them to lengthen. Compression stress is the opposite to tension stress. It is a pushing force, applied along the length of a tissue. When a person is standing upright the knee cartilages (menisci) take weight and compression stress is applied to them, causing them to flatten.

Shear stress occurs when opposite forces are applied to a tissue, causing one part of the tissue to slide over the other. For example, if an athlete who is running stops suddenly by digging their foot into the ground, shearing stress is applied to the knee. Body-weight tries to keep the athlete moving forwards, but – because the foot is fixed on the ground – the ground force pushes in the opposite direction. The result of these two opposing forces is shear.

Both compression and tension stresses act in line with the tissue fibres, in the direction in which the tissues are strongest. Shearing stresses, however, are imposed at an angle to the fibres, making this type of stress potentially the most dangerous in terms of injury. For example, a fall on to a straight leg will exert a compression stress on the joint structures. These forces will be largely absorbed, unless they are very severe. During the fall, tension stress will be imposed on the muscles if the joints bend. The elastic capabilities of the muscles will now take some of the stress away from the joint. Falling at an angle will again cause some compression and tension, but in addition shearing will take place between the body tissues, and the foot and ground. This type of stress can cause injury, and a fracture may result.

Tissue reaction to load

When a load is applied to a body tissue, the tissue will deform. The relationship between load and deformation can be represented graphically (*see* fig. 8). Initially when the load is applied the tissue demonstrates elasticity. This means that as the load is released the tissue returns to its original shape – it literally 'bounces back'. Because to begin with the amount of deformation is directly proportional to the load applied to the tissue, the start of the graph is straight. There is said to be a *linear relationship* between load and deformation at this point.

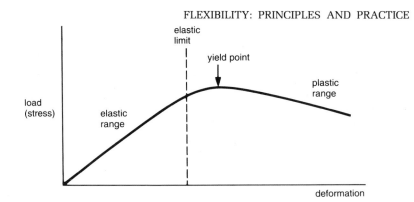

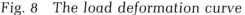

Fig. 8   *The load deformation curve*

If the load continues, the tissue is stretched beyond its elastic range and a point is reached at which deformation becomes permanent. Past this point, known as the *elastic limit*, the tissue will not return to its original shape when the load is released, and a permanent change has occurred. Instead of acting in an elastic fashion, the material is now said to be *viscous* or *plastic* in its reaction to load. The more load that is applied, the more deformed the material becomes. Instead of returning the load and bouncing back, the tissue is absorbing and dampening some of the load.

Eventually the yield point is reached, at the highest point of the graph. Now the material continues to deform even though the load applied to it is not increasing; in other words severe damage is occurring to the body tissue.

Body tissues combine both viscous and elastic properties, and so are termed *viscoelastic*. One of the essential features of the deformation of viscoelastic materials is that it is time dependent. This means that when a load is applied rapidly (sudden stretch) the deformation will be elastic, and the tissue will spring back. If the load is applied for some time (stretch and hold) the deformation becomes viscous, and the tissue will slowly 'give'.

Composition and resolution of forces

In figure 9(a) two men are pulling on ropes attached to a car bumper. Man A pulls at 45° to the car; man B also pulls at 45° but this time on the other side of the car. The net result is that the car rolls forwards. This process demonstrates the *composition of forces*. The forces supplied by the men pull at 90° to each other, combining to produce a third force – the *resultant* – which pulls the car forwards.

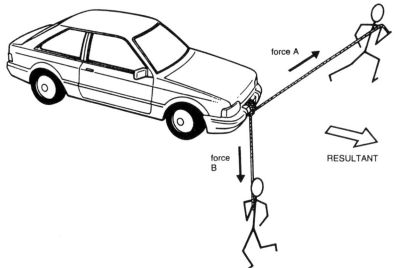

Fig. 9(a) Forces A and B combine to produce the resultant, which pulls the car forwards

Where we have just one force, we can use the reverse process to obtain the two original forces which make up the resultant. Now we are using the process of *resolution of forces* to more accurately demonstrate the effect of the force on the body. For example, when someone who is running places their foot on the ground a force known as the *ground reaction force* is created. This acts obliquely to the ground (*see* fig. 9(b)). This single force may be resolved into its two components, one of which acts vertically to create compression or jarring stress on the foot, while the other acts horizontally causing shearing or friction on the foot.

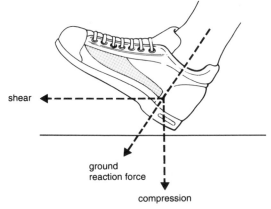

Fig. 9(b) The ground reaction force has two components, shear and compression

The composition of forces can also be important to stretching. Take as an example a quadriceps stretch (*see* pp. 89). As we bend the knee the top of the patella is pulled upwards along the length of the femur. The patella tendon pulls downwards, in the opposite direction. The result is a composition of these two forces to create a third force compressing the patella on to the femur below. This action can be very painful in someone suffering from inflammation of the front of the knee (*see* fig. 9(c)).

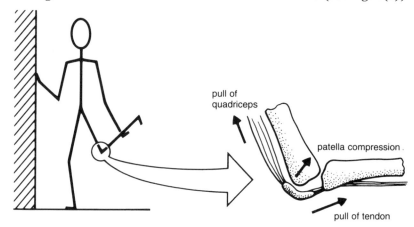

Fig. 9(c)   Patella compression can be very painful

Axes and planes

For descriptive purposes the human body may be divided into three planes. The *sagittal* plane passes through the body from front to back, dividing it into right and left halves. The *frontal* plane divides the body into anterior and posterior sections, and lies at right angles to the sagittal plane. The *transverse* plane divides the body into upper and lower portions, and rests at right angles to the other two planes.

Each of the three body planes has an associated axis which passes perpendicularly through it (*see* fig. 10). Movement occurs *in* a plane but *about* an axis. Abduction and adduction occur in the frontal plane about an anteroposterior (AP) axis; flexion and extension occur in a sagittal plane about a transverse axis; and rotations occur in a transverse plane about a vertical axis.

In reality movements do not just occur in one plane, but in several. This is because a complex series of movements link together to give a motion which occurs in all three planes about an oblique axis.

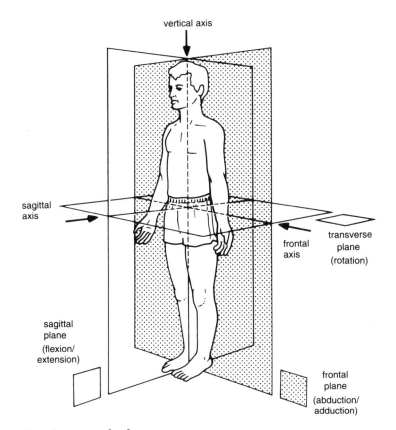

Fig. 10　*Axes and planes*

Anatomical terminology

Standard terminology should be used when describing body movements to avoid confusion. For example instead of 'bending' we use flexion, and instead of 'straightening' we use extension. Figure 11(a) shows the most commonly encountered terms.

To describe the position of part of the body we again use standard terminology. So, instead of saying 'in front' we use the term anterior, and instead of 'above', the term superior is used. Figure 11(b) shows the terms used most frequently.

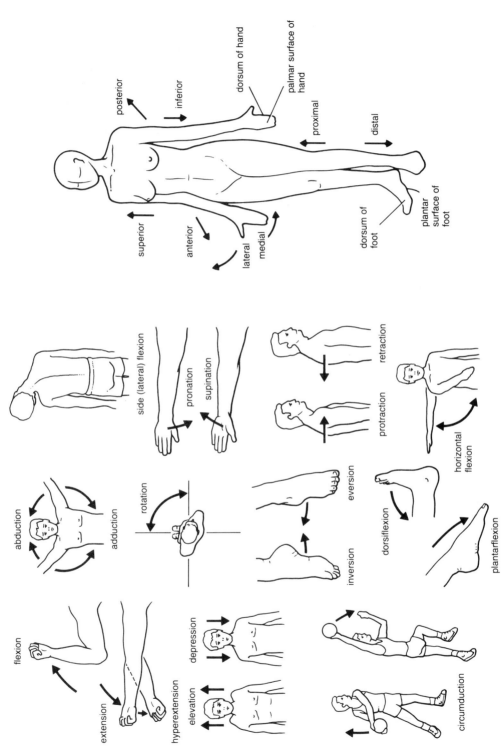

Fig. 11 (h)

Fig. 11 Anatomical terminology

Range of motion

The range of motion (ROM) of a muscle refers to the length of the muscle at any point in a movement. *Outer range* is from a fully stretched position to the mid-point of the movement. *Inner range* is from this mid-point to a fully shortened position of the muscle. *Mid-range* is an area between these two extremes and is the region in which most everyday actions occur (*see* fig. 12).

It is important that the body tissues are regularly taken through their full range of motion to maintain their extensibility and elasticity. When this does not occur, the muscle can shorten permanently, completely altering the function of a joint. For example, in a sedentary individual it is common for the hip flexors to become shortened, because most everyday movements only work these muscles within their inner range. The shortened muscle may then pull on to the lumbar spine, giving back-pain.

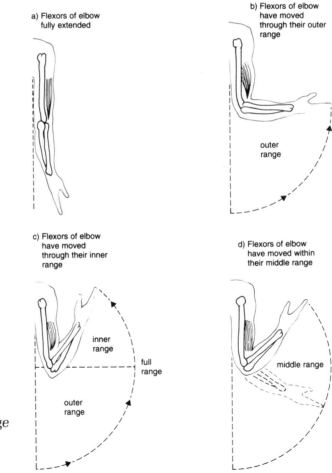

a) Flexors of elbow fully extended

b) Flexors of elbow have moved through their outer range

outer range

c) Flexors of elbow have moved through their inner range

inner range

full range

outer range

d) Flexors of elbow have moved within their middle range

middle range

Fig. 12 Range of motion

CHAPTER 2

Joint structure and function

The body has over 200 separate bones. Each is a rigid structure made from calcium, phosphorous and proteins. Bones may be divided into four major categories: long, short, flat and irregular.

The long bones are the type found in the limbs such as the thigh (femur) and upper arm (humerus). Their primary use is to act as levers for the muscles to pull on when producing movement.

Bone begins life as cartilage in the foetus. During the second month of pregnancy the cartilage bone begins to change into bone proper by a process known as *ossification* (see fig. 13). This begins in a primary centre in the middle of the bone and gradually spreads towards the bone ends. This central portion of ossified bone is called the *diaphysis*, while the end of the bone which is still made of cartilage is the *epiphysis*. During adolescence a secondary ossification centre appears in the epiphysis. Ossification here spreads towards the shaft, leaving a thin cartilage growth plate (epiphyseal plate) sandwiched between the two regions of ossified bone.

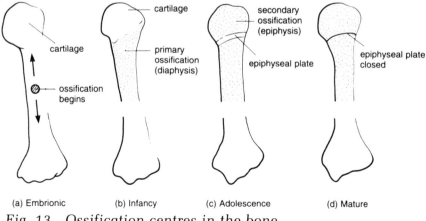

Fig. 13   *Ossification centres in the bone*

16

The growth plate is responsible for change in the length of the bone. As a person reaches maturity, the epiphyseal plate will disappear and the shaft and extremity of the bone fuse into one solid unit. The epiphyseal plate is an area of potential weakness in the young bone, and if damaged can result in permanent deformity of the bone. This is especially true of the upper part of the femur in sport, and great care must be taken when giving stretching exercises to children so that excessive strain is not imposed on the hip.

As a long bone ossifies, its shaft becomes a cylinder with hard compact bone on the outside surrounding a central medullary cavity. The bone cavity contains bone marrow, responsible for making blood cells. The epiphysis is made from spongy cancellous bone with a thin compact bone covering.

The other bone types do not contain a cavity but instead are made up of a honeycomb of cancellous bone with a thin compact bone covering. This makes them light although they may be bulky. Short bones are cube shaped and seen in the carpels of the hand and tarsals of the forefoot. Flat bones such as the scapulae and ribs form broad areas for muscle attachment, and serve to protect vital organs of the body. Irregular bones such as the vertebrae protect and support the body.

Joint types

In order for movement to occur in the body, the bones must articulate. The point at which this occurs is called a joint, and consists of two bones separated by various types of tissue. The shape of the bone-ends involved in a joint will dictate how much movement can occur, and which movement types are allowed. Joints may be broadly classified into three major groups, known as *fibrous* (immobile), *cartilaginous* (slightly mobile) and *synovial* (freely movable) – see table 1.

Fibrous joints

Fibrous joints allow little, if any, movement. Examples include the joints formed between the bones of the skull (a suture joint), those of the teeth (a gomphosis), and the 'syndesmosis', an example of which is found between the upper end of the fibula and the upper outer aspect of the tibia.

The edges of the bones forming the suture joints of the skull are jagged, and separated by fibrous tissue. This type of joint will not normally allow any perceptible movement, and may close up completely after the age of 30.

Table 1   Joint types

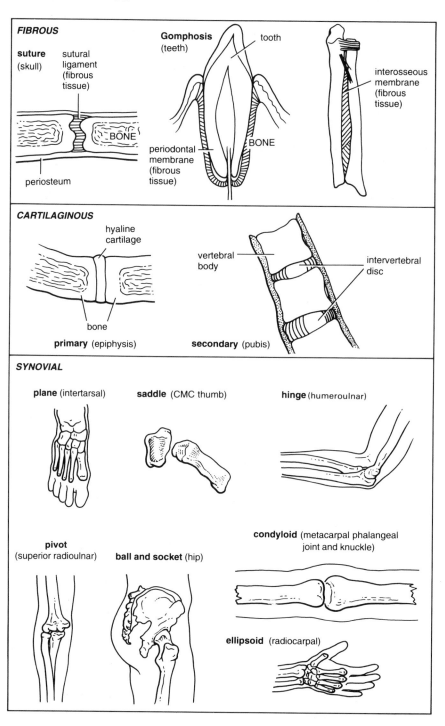

FIBROUS

suture (skull)   sutural ligament (fibrous tissue)

Gomphosis (teeth)   tooth

interosseous membrane (fibrous tissue)

BONE

periodontal membrane (fibrous tissue)   BONE

periosteum

CARTILAGINOUS

hyaline cartilage

vertebral body   intervertebral disc

bone

primary (epiphysis)   **secondary** (pubis)

SYNOVIAL

plane (intertarsal)   **saddle** (CMC thumb)   **hinge** (humeroulnar)

condyloid (metacarpal phalangeal joint and knuckle)

pivot (superior radioulnar)   **ball and socket** (hip)

ellipsoid (radiocarpal)

The syndesmosis is again separated by fibrous tissue, but more than in the suture joint. The fibrous tissue in this joint forms into a ligament which allows small amounts of twisting and stretching movements. The tooth joint or 'gomphosis' consists of a peg which fits tightly into a socket, held in place by a fibrous band.

Cartilaginous joints

In cartilaginous joints the bones are separated by a pad of cartilage tissue, and both primary and secondary types exist. The primary cartilaginous joint has hyaline cartilage separating the bones. They occur as the growth plates at the end of bones in children. At the beginning of adult life the growth plate closes and the two pieces of bone (the diaphysis and epiphysis) become one.

The secondary cartilaginous joints are found in the centre line of the body; examples include the spinal discs and the joint between the two pubic bones (known as the symphysis pubis). The bone-ends of the joint are separated from each other by a fibrocartilage pad, a structure which allows limited movement.

Synovial joints

The synovial joints are the ones we are most concerned with when using stretching exercises. They are freely movable, and contain a variety of joint structures. A typical synovial joint consists of two bone-ends covered by articular (hyaline) cartilage.

The joint is surrounded by a fibrous joint capsule. Certain portions of the capsule are thickened to form supporting ligaments. The capsule is lined with a thin synovial membrane which secretes a lubricating liquid called *synovial fluid*. Structures inside the joint or within the capsule are known as 'intracapsular'. Structures associated with the joint but found outside the capsule are called 'extracapsular'. These include small balloon-like pads or 'bursae' which stop structures rubbing over each other, and small 'fat pads' which fill the gaps between tissues.

Muscles control the joint (*see* page 26), and those passing close to the bones may attach some fibres to the joint structures. For example, the popliteus muscle of the knee also attaches to the medial knee ligament and medial knee meniscus.

There are seven main types of synovial joint (*see* table 1). The *plane* joint has relatively flat surfaces and permits gliding or twisting of one bone against the other. The intertarsal joints of the foot are examples of plane joints. The *saddle* joint has one convex surface and one concave surface arranged at right angles to each other, as with a horse rider sitting in a saddle. The major movements occur in two planes, with a slight amount of combined movement occurring in a third plane. An example is the carpometacarpal joint of the thumb. The *hinge* allows movement in one axis only, and a strong joint is formed, with tight ligaments. An example is the elbow joint, formed between the humerus and ulna. The *pivot* joint allows a rotation movement about one axis only. One piece of bone rotates in a ring formed by the other bone and ligament tissue. An example is the joint formed between the radius and the ulna in the elbow (superior radioulnar joint).

The *ball and socket* joint allows movement in all three planes, examples being the hip and shoulder joints. A ball-shaped surface of one bone articulates with a cup-shaped surface of the other. The *condyloid* joint is similar to the ball and socket, but allows movement in only two planes. The metacarpophalangeal (MCP) joints of the fingers are examples. The *ellipsoid* joint is again a modification of the ball and socket. The convex surface of one bone is oval in shape, while the concave surface of the opposing bone is elliptical. The radiocarpal joint in the wrist is an example here.

Individual differences in joint structure

Although each person has the same joint types, there is tremendous variation in the general structure and function of joints between two individuals. The shapes of the bones will vary. This can be due to hereditary influences, physical training or injury. Some people are naturally more or less flexible because of the shape of their bones. Those who have exercised regularly since an early age will be considerably different from inactive individuals. For example, girls who have spent many years practising ballet as children will tend to be more flexible around the hips for the rest of their lives.

Injury and disease will also affect the range of motion which is possible at a joint. Older athletes who have varying amounts of arthritis will show reduced movement in specific patterns. For example, lateral rotation of the shoulder and hip tends to be very limited. Where an injury has occurred in early life the growth plate in a bone may have been affected. A severe fall from a bicycle or horse can often dislodge a bony growth plate and alter the formation of the final mature bone.

The structural differences at a joint must be appreciated when comparing ranges of movement between individuals. Even with the same amount of training, two people may never gain the same amount of movement at a joint.

Joint structures

Articular cartilage

The ends of the bones forming a joint are covered by hyaline cartilage. This is a substance made from a gel-like material containing fibres. It is about 70–80% water and has no blood vessels or nerves, relying instead for its nutrition on the synovial fluid. Substances move into and out of the cartilage by diffusion from the synovial fluid, a process heavily reliant on regular movement to cause alterations in pressure within the fluid. As the cartilage is compressed intermittently with movement, for example walking or running, nutrients are pumped into and out of the cartilage. With continuous loading such as occurs in prolonged standing, the cartilage is compressed further and further without allowing more fluid to be taken up. This continual compression without release can reduce the cartilage depth by as much as 40%.

The area of cartilage next to the bone (the sub-chondral region) is firmly attached to the bone and will resist shearing forces. The main body of the cartilage contains fibres which will resist tension stresses, while the fluid within the cartilage gel resists compression. The fibres are elastic, and the gel will gradually flow away from any compressing force, the combination of these two reactions giving cartilage a viscoelastic property.

The joint capsule

The joint capsule is composed of two parts. The outer portion (stratum fibrosum) is tough and fibrous and is thickened in certain areas to form ligaments. The inner portion of the capsule (stratum synoviale) is loose and contains many blood vessels. This region blends with the synovial membrane of the joint.

The capsule is attached to the bones around the edge of the joint, and at the line of attachments many small blood vessels are seen. The capsule has a rich supply of nerve fibres responsible for the 'joint sense' (proprioception) used in balance and reflex actions. The capsule is particularly important after injury. Following joint sprains, the joint will swell, and the accumulation of fluid will stretch the capsule causing tightness and pain. After injury the capsule can thicken and further limit the joint movement, requiring specialist physiotherapy techniques and regular stretching exercises to regain the lost movement.

Synovial membrane

The synovial membrane lines the joint capsule and consists of two distinct layers. The inner layer secretes the synovial fluid, while the outer layer is a loose, highly vascular structure consisting of collagen fibres and fat cells. This outer layer merges with the membrane covering the bones, the *periosteum*.

The blood vessels of the joint divide into three branches, one travelling to the epiphysis at the end of the bone, the second to the joint capsule, and the third to the synovial membrane itself. The blood vessels contained in the synovial membrane can exchange fluid and nutrient molecules with the synovial fluid.

The synovial membrane has a series of folds in it. As the joint moves, it will unfold like a fan to allow movement (rather than simply stretching). The folds of the synovial membrane have extensive lubrication to virtually eliminate friction.

Ligaments

Many ligaments are simply parts of the joint capsule which have thickened to resist particular stresses on the joints. They are made of connective tissue fibres, and attach to the bones of the joint. The ligament fibres are arranged along the lines of stress imposed on the joint. As a joint is moved the ligaments will stretch, initially pulling the fibres straight and then stretching them. Exercise will regularly lengthen the ligaments and strengthen them, but stretching exercises which overstress the ligaments shouid be avoided. The ligaments support the joint, and if overstretched can leave the joint too flexible causing it to be insecure and open to injury. Following a ligament injury, it is particularly important to keep the joint moving gently, so that the newly healing ligament fibres will again align themselves correctly rather than in a haphazard fashion.

Ligaments at the side of the joint (collateral ligaments) resist stresses which would tend to open the joint sideways. Other ligaments are positioned to protect the joint in its most vulnerable movements.

Muscle–tendon unit

The muscles are attached to the bones via a tendon. This is an inelastic collagen structure which simply transmits the force created by the muscle to the bone in order to move it. The tendon is able to transmit the force to a small area, keeping the bulk of the muscle away from the joint. Some tendons, such as those of the finger muscles, are very long, allowing the muscles to be positioned in the forearm, well away from the finger joint where the muscle force is applied. Other tendons, such as that of the deltoid muscle of the shoulder, are directly next to the muscle itself.

The thick central part of the muscle is called the muscle *belly*, and it is the part which bulges as the muscle contracts. The muscle tapers down towards the tendon, the area between the muscle and tendon being the musculo-tendinous junction. The tendon inserts into the bone via the teno-osseous junction.

Joint lubrication

The joint cartilage has no blood supply. As we have seen, it relies for its nutrition largely on materials being passed from the synovial fluid. Movement will flush fresh fluid over the cartilage surface, and alterations in pressure will press nutrients into the cartilage. If the joint does not move properly, for example following injury, nutrient material may not be pressed into the cartilage, and that area may degenerate giving osteoarthritis.

The synovial fluid provides a lubricating mechanism which cuts down the amount of friction the joint is subjected to. As the two bony surfaces move over each other, the small synovial fluid molecules act as tiny ball-bearings preventing the opposing cartilage surfaces from rubbing away. Some of the fluid is absorbed into the cartilage almost like water in a sponge. As pressure is exerted on the joint when standing or walking, for example, the fluid is squeezed out of the cartilage forming a fluid film which separates the cartilage surfaces and again prevents them rubbing.

It is often said (usually by inactive individuals) that exercise causes arthritis. This is far from the case. Movement will actually keep the joint cartilage healthy, and is essential for the general health of the joint. However, if an injury occurs and an athlete tries to 'train through the pain', the biomechanics of the joint will be altered and changes may occur in the joint cartilage, ultimately leading to the development of arthritis. In addition, a balance must be kept between the strength of muscles supporting a joint and the flexibility of the joint structures. If a person becomes too flexible the joint will not be secure. Similarly, if a person has too little flexibility their joints will be stiff. Either case will alter the normal biomechanics of a joint and could give problems later in life.

Joint mechanics

Physiological and accessory movements

Two major types of movement are possible at any joint. First, there are the normal actions which an athlete controls, such as flexion and extension. These are known as *physiological* movements. But there are also *accessory* movements, which cannot be produced directly but occur automatically as a joint moves, giving 'joint play'. For example, as the knee bends and straightens, the femur and tibia will also glide and roll on each other. The bending and straightening (flexion and extension) are the physiological movements, while the gliding and rolling are the accessory movements. Three distinct types of accessory movements occur, known as *roll*, *slide* and *spin*.

Roll is similar to a car tyre rolling over the road surface. At any point, areas on the tyre will be in contact with the same areas on the road surface (see fig. 14(a)). If slide occurs, a single point on one surface will be in contact with a number of other points on the opposing surface, as when a car tyre skids (see fig 14(b)). Spin occurs when both points on the two opposing surfaces are in contact, and pure rotation occurs as with a 'spinning top' (see fig 14(c)).

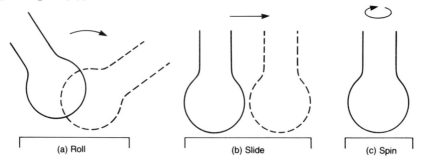

| (a) Roll | (b) Slide | (c) Spin |

Fig. 14   Accessory movements in a joint

Accessory movements become important to general flexibility after injury. If a joint is stiff, stretching it will regain the physiological movements but may not bring back the accessory movements. This can leave the joint feeling awkward and open to injury. For this reason, it is always wise to see a physiotherapist after a sports injury to have the joint movement properly assessed.

Close and loose pack

The two opposing surfaces of a joint do not fit together exactly
– they are said to be *non-congruent*. However, with the joint in
one particular position its surfaces will come as close together
as they are able, and this is known as 'close pack'. In this
position the joint capsule and ligaments twist and pull the joint
surfaces tightly together. The joint space is at a minimum, the
concave surface of one bone fits closely on to the convex shape
of the other, and no further movement is possible. In the close-
pack position, stress will be taken on the bones in a fall because
the ligaments in a joint are fully tightened and unable to 'give'
any more. A fracture is often the result.

Loose-pack position is exactly the opposite. As the joint
surfaces are released from their close-pack position, elastic recoil
of the soft tissues surrounding the joint enables its surfaces to
move apart, maximising the joint space. The joint will be less
secure in this position and more movement will be possible.
Should the athlete fall with the joint in a loose-pack position,
the joint will often move too much, and ligament injury can
result.

CHAPTER 3

Muscle action

How muscles work

If we take a small piece of muscle tissue and magnify it many times (see fig. 15), we can see that it is made up of many long muscle fibres. Each individual muscle fibre is surrounded by a thin membrane, and in turn the fibres are grouped together in bundles. Finally, the whole muscle structure is encased in a sheath.

Looking closely at each fibre, we see alternating light and dark bands, corresponding to different muscle proteins (see fig. 15(c)). The light area is composed of a thin filament called *actin*, while the dark area consists of a thicker filament called *myosin*. The two sets of filaments fit together like the fingers on two opposing hands, one set of actin–myosin fibres being called a *sarcomere* (see fig. 15(e)). The thick myosin filament has projections or 'crossbridges' coming from it much like the oars of a boat. Further examination of the muscle reveals a network of tiny tubes running into the muscle fibres. These tubes spread chemicals from the outside of the muscle to its centre.

Contraction of the muscle occurs when the muscle filaments move towards each other. When we want a muscle to contract, a nervous impulse is sent from the brain. This impulse travels down the spinal cord and along a peripheral nerve to the muscle, where it causes changes on the surface of the muscle fibre. As a result, chemicals travel down the muscle-fibre tubes and into the fibre itself. This causes a chemical reaction which activates the filament crossbridges. These pull the muscle filaments closer together, causing them to slide over each other and shorten the muscle.

The whole muscle contraction process uses energy, and rest is needed to recharge the structures involved. Chemicals have to

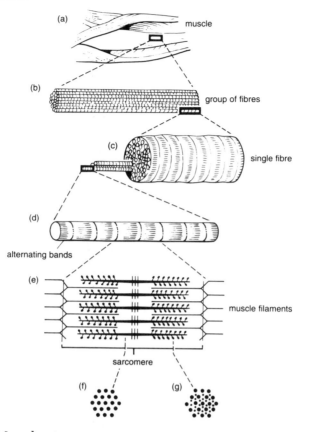

Fig. 15   Muscle structure

be moved out of the muscle, and the filaments must return to their original relaxed positions.

Muscle reflexes

Three muscle reflexes are important when using flexibility training: the stretch reflex; autogenic inhibition (also known as the reverse stretch reflex); and reciprocal innervation.

The stretch reflex is important both for postural control and muscle tone. It relies on information coming from special receptors called *muscle spindles* (*see* fig. 16). The muscle spindle is a cigar-shaped structure attached alongside the main muscle fibres. When the muscle is stretched, so is the muscle spindle. The stretch of the spindle is detected by nerves and a reflex occurs which causes the muscle to contract and so shorten the spindle once more.

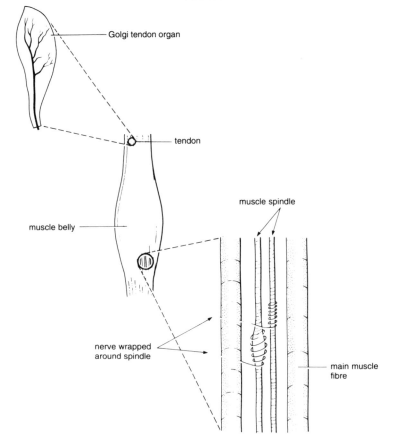

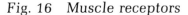

Fig. 16   *Muscle receptors*

The stretch reflex reacts to change in both the length of the muscle and in the velocity of its movement. Change in length is important for postural or 'tonic' control, while change in velocity is important for movement or 'phasic' control. The classic example of the stretch reflex acting for phasic control is the knee jerk, or patellar reflex. Here, the patella tendon is stretched rapidly by being hit with a small rubber hammer. This rapid stretch is picked up by the muscle spindles in the quadriceps and causes nerve impulses to be sent to the spinal cord. Impulses return from the cord to the quadriceps causing them to contract, and the knee straightens quickly giving a small 'kick'.

The stretch reflex is also essential for the maintenance of normal standing posture, through tonic control. When we stand up we continually sway forwards and back. As we start to fall forwards there is a pull on our calf muscles, changing their length and causing a stretch reflex. The calf muscles then contract a split-second later to pull us back to the upright position again.

Another receptor, the *golgi tendon organ* (GTO), is situated in the muscle tendon (*see* fig. 16). This receptor measures tension. When a muscle contracts it shortens, and so a stretch reflex will not occur. However, the GTO will register the increasing tension in the muscle tendon and will then cause a reflex relaxation of the muscle, a process known as *autogenic inhibition*. This is the reverse situation to the stretch reflex, and has a protective function, preventing the muscle from contracting so hard that it pulls its attachment off the bone. The two reflexes do not occur at the same time, because the threshold of the GTO is set far higher than that of the muscle spindle. In normal everyday movement, tension in the muscle is not high enough to cause autogenic inhibition.

Both of these reflexes have important implications for stretching exercises. Stretching which involves short jerking movements will tighten the muscle through the stretch reflex, while sustained stretching (over about 10 seconds) will allow the muscle to relax. Relaxation occurs because the stretch reflex becomes desensitised, and if the muscle tension is high enough autogenic inhibition follows through stimulation of the GTO. The autogenic inhibition in this case overrides the stretch reflex.

A further reflex is called *reciprocal innervation*. This occurs when the antagonist muscle relaxes to allow the prime mover to create a movement. For example, when the biceps contracts to bend the elbow, the triceps will relax through reciprocal innervation to allow the movement to occur. This reflex can be used to obtain further relaxation in a muscle just prior to stretching.

Elastic properties of muscle

Muscle has three properties: contractability, extensibility and elasticity. The contractile nature of muscle results from the movement of the sliding filaments within the muscle fibre. When the actin and myosin filaments come together, force is generated and the muscle will shorten. If the muscle filaments shorten, but the external length of the muscle remains the same, the muscle tenses but the joint on which the muscle works will not move. This is an isometric or static muscle contraction. An example is holding an object in the hand with the elbow bent to 90°.

When the muscle filaments shorten and pull the attachments of the muscle closer to each other, causing movement at the joint, the muscle contraction is then concentric. In our example above, instead of the arm being held still, the elbow joint flexes.

Once the elbow has been flexed, and the muscle filaments have shortened, lowering the weight again involves the muscle filaments slowly paying out to control the joint as it extends. This is an eccentric action. This type of action is used to slow the body down and control movements such as sitting down into a chair or coming downstairs. Each time, the muscle filaments are sliding apart and the muscle is lengthening.

We have seen that the bundles of muscle fibres are surrounded by connective tissue sheaths. These cannot contract, but they will stretch, and have important elastic properties. These elements of the muscle are known as the *parallel elastic components* because they are aligned in parallel to the muscle fibres. The tendons at the end of the muscle are also non-contractile, but

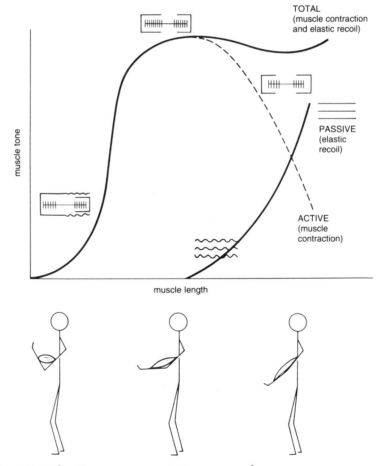

Fig. 17   *Elastic components in a muscle*

again they show elastic properties. These are the *series elastic components*, so called because they are positioned before and after the fibres (*see* fig. 17).

We know that there is a linear relationship between load and elasticity from the load-deformation curve (*see* page 10). As we load a muscle it will stretch proportionally; and as the stretch ceases and the muscle springs back, energy is released. So, the force produced as a muscle is released from being stretched is a combination of elastic and contractile properties (*see* fig. 17).

When we lengthen a muscle the muscle filaments move apart, ready to contract once more, and the elastic elements of the muscle are stretched. If this stretch is applied rapidly a stretch reflex occurs, causing the muscle to tighten and pull against the stretching force. If the muscle is contracted immediately afterwards the contractile force produced will be a summation of contraction, elasticity, and reflex mechanisms and will be far greater than if the muscle contracted from rest (*see* fig. 18). This type of pre-stretching is used to advantage in plyometric training where a series of jumps and bounding movements are used to build up 'elastic strength'.

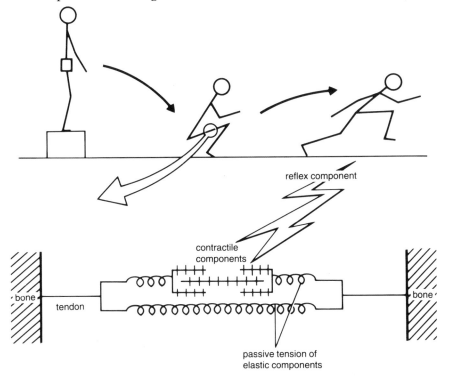

reflex component

contractile components

bone

tendon

bone

passive tension of elastic components

Fig. 18   Developing elastic stretch

Muscle-fibre type and arrangement

All muscles contain fibres of different types. Red fibres are designed to contract over and over again without fatiguing, and are known as 'slow-twitch' fibres. White fibres are called 'fast twitch', and these give short bursts of power. A person's muscles will contain both fibre types but in different proportions. Those who are good at endurance sports tend to have more slow-twitch fibres in the leg muscles, while those who perform explosive sprints have more fast-twitch fibres (see fig. 19).

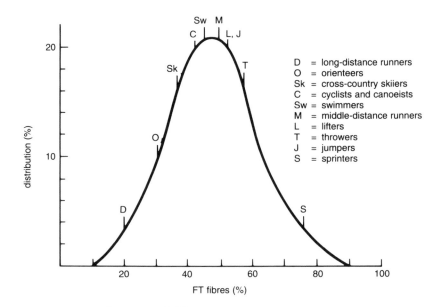

Fig. 19   Distribution of fibre types

No matter which type is present, each fibre is only able to shorten and reduce its length by half. Although the same amount of shortening occurs with each fibre, altering the arrangement of these fibres within a muscle will affect muscle function. Two different arrangements are found, one for short powerful muscles and the other for long flexible ones.

The short powerful type is like the deltoid muscle of the shoulder. Here, the fibres are arranged side by side, inserting into a central tendon like the barbs on a feather. There are many of them so the muscle is very powerful. However, the fibres are short so the muscle cannot move very far and is therefore comparatively inflexible. This type of arrangement is called 'pennate' (see fig. 20).

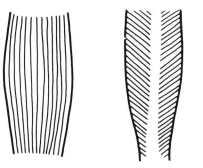

a) Long fibres of parallel muscle   b) Shorter fibres of pennate muscle

Fig. 20   Arrangement of muscle fibres

Long slender muscles like the hamstrings on the back of the leg have their fibres arranged parallel to each other, attaching to tendons at each end. There are fewer fibres so the muscle is less powerful than before. However, the muscle will still shorten by half, and as this type of muscle is much longer the movement it produces will be of a greater range.

When choosing stretching exercises it is important to be aware of the underlying muscle structure to devise more effective programmes.

How strong a muscle is will be partially determined by its length at rest. A muscle is strongest when it is contracted from a resting stretched state (*see* fig. 21). If the muscle is shortened, less tension can be exerted. This is because an overlap of the muscle filaments occurs, interfering with the contraction. If the muscle is overstretched, the filaments are pulled completely apart and no tension can be developed.

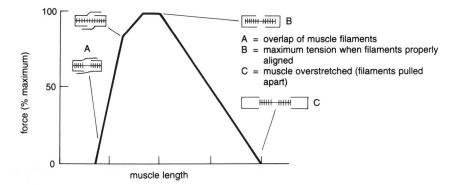

A = overlap of muscle filaments
B = maximum tension when filaments properly aligned
C = muscle overstretched (filaments pulled apart)

Fig. 21   Length–tension relationship of a muscle

If we are throwing an object or hitting a ball we often need to develop the maximal amount of force possible. The amount of force will be dependent on our underlying strength, but also on the flexibility of a muscle and on the range of motion through which a limb is taken. This is because when we are able to use a greater range of motion we have more time to allow the speed of an object to build up. Take as an example the javelin throw. If an athlete has very stiff shoulders he or she will not be able to take the javelin very far back. An athlete with good flexibility around the shoulders will be able to develop greater force by accelerating the javelin for a longer period.

Postural changes which shorten or lengthen a muscle over a period of time will also alter a muscle's strength through the above mechanism. If a muscle is held in a shortened position it will eventually tighten because the actin and myosin filaments of the muscle move together and the muscle sheath shrinks. The overlap of muscle fibres which occurs makes the muscle weaker. The lengthening of a muscle over a period of time comes about through the addition of more sarcomeres. In this case, although the muscle has been lengthened, the sarcomere length has been reduced and the muscle is again weak. These two instances represent the so-called 'positional weakness' of a muscle and are important factors in posture and muscle imbalance (see page 59).

Group action of muscles

A muscle can only pull, it cannot decide which action to perform. We produce an infinite variety of actions with a finite number of muscles by combining the various actions in different ways. This co-ordinated action of the various muscles working on a body-part is called the 'group action of muscles'.

When a muscle pulls to create a movement it is said to be acting as a *prime mover* or *agonist*. Most muscles can take on this function, depending on the action required and the site of the muscle. The muscle which would oppose the prime mover if it contracted is known as the *antagonist*. If we bend the arm the biceps will act as the prime mover to create the power necessary to carry out the movement. To allow the movement to occur, however, the opposite muscle – in this case the triceps – must relax and in so doing acts as an antagonist (see fig. 22(a)).

Muscles do not simply create movements; they are also able to stabilise parts of the body or prevent unwanted actions by acting as fixators. In this case the muscle will contract to steady or support the bone on to which the prime mover attaches.

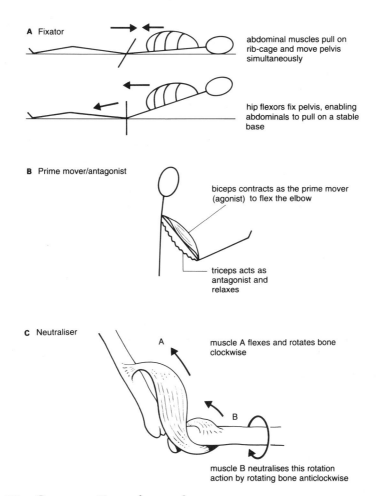

A Fixator

abdominal muscles pull on
rib-cage and move pelvis
simultaneously

hip flexors fix pelvis, enabling
abdominals to pull on a stable
base

B Prime mover/antagonist

biceps contracts as the prime mover
(agonist) to flex the elbow

triceps acts as
antagonist and
relaxes

C Neutraliser

A

muscle A flexes and rotates bone
clockwise

B

muscle B neutralises this rotation
action by rotating bone anticlockwise

Fig. 22   Group action of muscles

Take as an example the sit-up exercise. The abdominal muscles
attach from the rib-cage to the pelvis, and so when they contract
they will move both body areas. To allow the abdominals to
contract more effectively we need to fix one body area to provide
a firm base for the muscle to pull on. This occurs by the hip
flexor muscles acting as fixators to stop the pelvis from tilting as
the abdominals contract (see fig. 22(b)).

Many muscles can perform more than one movement. In the
case of the biceps, for example, as well as flexing the elbow the
muscle can also twist the forearm upwards (supination). If we
want the biceps to perform just one action, bending the arm but
not twisting it, other muscles must contract to stop the biceps
from twisting the forearm. These muscles, which eliminate

unwanted actions, are acting as *neutralisers* (*see* fig. 22(c)). As we saw above, the biceps muscle cannot decide which action to perform and which not to perform. Again it must be emphasised that a muscle can only pull: if we want to alter the action it will produce we must bring other muscles into play as neutralisers.

Two-joint muscles

Some muscles cross over two joints, and are said to be *biarticular*. The hamstrings, for example, attach from the seat bone (ischial tuberosity) to the top of the tibia. Because they cross both the hip and knee joints they are capable of creating, or limiting, movement at both joints. Other muscles which are biarticular include rectus femoris and gastrocnemius in the lower limb, and biceps and triceps in the upper limb.

Biarticular muscles have a number of important biomechanical features. First, because they pass over two joints, they cannot shorten enough to allow full movement at both joints simultaneously. For example, with the knee bent and the hamstrings relaxed at the knee the hip can flex maximally enabling the knee to be pulled right up on to the chest (*see* fig. 23(a)). However, with the knee straight, and the lower portion of the hamstrings stretched, hip flexion is more limited (*see* fig. 23(b)). This limitation of movement at both joints is called *passive insufficiency*.

If you stand up and flex your hip you will be able to bend your knee actively to touch your heel on to your buttock (*see* fig. 23(c)). If you pull your hip into extension first, however, and try the same movement, you will find that you are unable to touch your heel to your buttock (*see* fig. 23(d)). This is because in the first example the upper portion of the hamstrings was lengthened and the lower part shortened. In the second example, the upper and lower parts of the muscle are unable to shorten fully at the same time. This inability to create full movement at both joints simultaneously is called *active insufficiency*.

Because biarticular muscles are unable to permit full movement at both joints at the same time, the tension in one muscle will cause tension to build up in its antagonist. For example, if the hamstrings contract and extend the hip they will stretch the rectus femoris which is acting as an antagonist. The stretch in the rectus will then tend to pull the knee straight and extend it. When both the hip and knee are extending in this fashion, *concurrent movement* is said to be occurring. If we look at what happens to the muscle we can see that this type of action actually

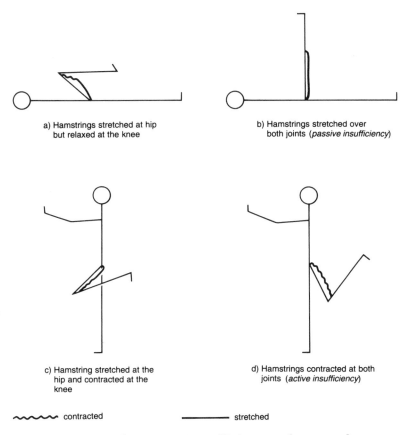

a) Hamstrings stretched at hip
but relaxed at the knee

b) Hamstrings stretched over
both joints (*passive insufficiency*)

c) Hamstring stretched at the
hip and contracted at the
knee

d) Hamstrings contracted at both
joints (*active insufficiency*)

～～～ contracted   ——————— stretched

Fig. 23   *Active and passive insufficiency of a muscle*

conserves energy. The hip and knee are both extending, so the
hamstrings are shortened at their upper end and lengthened at
their lower. The rectus femoris is also shortened at its upper end
and lengthened lower down. This action has therefore avoided
both active and passive insufficiency, by neither shortening nor
stretching both ends of either muscle. It is used in running as we
push off from the ground.

In a kicking action the opposite occurs. When the hip is
flexed and the knee extended both the upper and lower portions
of the rectus femoris are shortened, while both parts of the
hamstrings are lengthened. The rectus therefore rapidly loses
tension while the hamstrings rapidly gain tension, an example
of *countercurrent movement*.

Postural and phasic muscles

Muscles in general can be categorised into two distinct groups: those responsible for posture (tonic); and those more active in explosive movements (phasic) – *see* table 2. Postural muscles have a tendency to become tight following injury and also during exercise. These muscles are usually biarticular, and proportionally stronger than their phasic counterparts. As well as reducing range of motion, the tightened muscle is more likely to develop painful trigger points. In addition, tight muscles tend to be activated earlier than they should in a movement sequence, making the movement look clumsy.

Table 2 Postural and phasic muscles

POSTURAL	PHASIC
MUSCLES	
Gastro-soleus	Peronei
Tibialis posterior	Tibialis anterior
Short hip adductors	Vastus medialis and lateralis
Hamstrings	Gluteals
Rectus femoris	Abdominal muscles
Iliopsoas	Serratus anterior
Tensor fasciae latae	Rhomboids
Piriformis	Lower portion trapezius
Erector spinae	Short cervical flexors
	Extensors of upper limb
Quadratus lumborum	
Pectoralis major	
Upper portion of trapezius	
Levator scapulae	
Sternomastoid	
Scalenes	
Flexors of the upper limb	
CHARACTERISTICS	
Tend to tighten	Tend to lengthen
Biarticular	Weak
One third stronger	Uniarticular
Trigger points	
Lower irritability threshold	

Phasic muscles are antagonistic to the postural type, and show a tendency to weaken and lengthen with inactivity and also following injury. The lengthening of the muscle over a period of time gives rise to positional weakness.

The reasons for the differences between postural and phasic muscle types are quite complex. There is an alteration in the nervous control to the muscles. An extreme example of this is seen in a person who has had a stroke, where it is the postural muscles which become very tight or 'spastic'. In addition, postural muscles have a greater proportion of slow-twitch fibres, while phasic muscles contain more fast-twitch fibres.

A subtle relationship exists between postural and phasic muscles. Normally, the agonist and antagonist muscles surrounding a joint are of roughly equal strength and flexibility. However, when a muscle becomes tight it can do so because the number of nerve impulses travelling to it increases, raising the muscle tone. If the tone of the agonist muscle increases, the tone of the antagonist will reduce through reciprocal innervation (*see* page 29). The muscle with the lower tone appears weaker because it is inhibited, and we call this process 'pseudoparesis'. Attempts to strengthen a muscle weakened in this way can be ineffective. However, stretching the antagonist muscle can release the inhibition of the agonist and its normal strength returns quickly. This is an important characteristic of the muscle imbalance process (*see* page 59).

CHAPTER 4

Training principles

Warm-up

Before starting any exercise period, it is essential to warm up. There are two main reasons for this. First, warming up can make sports injuries less likely in certain circumstances. Second, the body works more efficiently when warm and so sports performance may actually improve. A good warm-up will have physiological, mechanical and psychological effects.

Physiological effects

It takes some time for the body to change from its basic 'tick over' at rest to a point at which it is ready to perform maximally. If vigorous exercise is started immediately from rest, the heartbeat is speeded up with a jolt instead of increasing gradually, and the beats of the heart can become irregular rather than showing their normal smooth rhythm. These changes affecting the heart can be potentially very serious in the older or less active individual, and especially in those with a history of heart or circulatory problems.

A warm-up will allow the body tissues to work more efficiently. Normally, while relaxed, the muscles receive only about 15% of the total amount of blood. The rest goes to the body organs such as the brain, liver and intestines. During vigorous exercise, because the muscles need far more fuel to provide energy, their requirement for blood increases so that they now need 80% of the total blood flow. It takes time to re-route this blood by opening some blood vessels and closing others, and if the muscles are required to perform maximally before the blood flow has changed they will work inefficiently.

Incidentally, this process of alteration in regional blood flow is the reason why you should not exercise within an hour of eating a heavy meal. After eating, we need the blood to stay in the region of the stomach and intestines to effectively absorb the digested foodstuffs. If we start to exercise during this period, much of the blood will move away from the digestive organs and into the working muscles. The result can be digestive upsets and 'stomach cramps'.

The body can produce energy by two methods, aerobically (with oxygen) and anaerobically (without oxygen). The aerobic method is preferable because when we work anaerobically we produce a waste product called lactic acid. Unfortunately we cannot work aerobically straightaway: it takes time to switch the aerobic system on. If we start intense exercise without a warm-up, the aerobic system does not have enough time to switch on; we therefore have to provide energy anaerobically, with resultant lactic acid formation.

The function of a warm-up is to 'switch on' the aerobic system and allow the body to reach a steady state where the energy provided by the body exactly matches its requirements through exercise. Once this is done, less waste is produced and so our recovery after exercise will be much faster.

Mechanical effects

The mechanical effects of warm-up occur as a direct result of tissue heating. Chemical reactions involved in the production of energy for the working muscle and the removal of waste products are speeded up with warmth. In addition, nervous impulses travel faster when a nerve is warm. The effects of warm-up on nerve conduction is particularly important for the speed of reflexes which protect the muscles from injury.

When a substance is heated it becomes more pliable, and this is exactly the same for the body tissues. We have seen that there is a relationship between load and deformation of a tissue (see fig. 8, page 10). One of the effects of warm-up is to move the load–deformation curve to the right. This means that, for any given load, a warm tissue will be elastic for longer and will reach its failure point later. The effect of these changes is to make stretching exercises both more effective and safer. In addition, the fluid within a joint becomes less stiff (viscous) when warm and so the joint will move more smoothly.

Because tissues will stretch more easily after a warm-up, it is important that stretching exercises are not performed at the beginning of a warm-up period. Vigorously touching the toes will not act as a warm-up for the hamstrings, and may tear them instead!

Psychological effects

Two effects are important here: arousal level and mental rehearsal. There is a direct relationship between arousal and performance, and this can be illustrated on the 'human performance curve' (see fig. 24). Initially, as arousal increases so does performance.

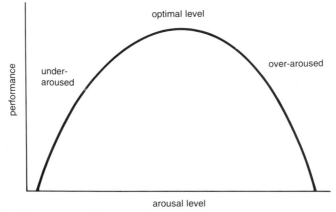

Fig. 24   Human performance curve

However, after a certain point an individual becomes too aroused (they are now 'stressed') and their performance suffers. As an illustration of this mechanism, imagine you have had a boring day and you arrive at the gym not really wanting to exercise. Your arousal level is low and so your exercise performance will be poor. If you then go into an exercise class, however, the instructor, the music and the other people will increase your arousal level. You feel motivated and your exercise performance improves. On the other hand again, if you are an athlete competing in an important game you may miss a shot which normally you would find very easy. Perhaps you are nervous, your heart is pounding and your arousal level is too high, so your performance suffers.

The function of a warm-up should be to place an athlete at the optimum point on the human performance curve, and this will change depending on the individual and the sport. A person who is very introverted and underaroused may need to be 'psyched up' in a warm-up to move them to the right on the curve. Someone who is aggressive, extrovert and 'hyperactive' may need to be settled down and moved further to the left on the curve. Events which require highly skilled movements tend to be performed better at lower levels of arousal, when an athlete is calm and can focus his or her attention. Events which require power or explosive· actions are normally performed better when higher levels of arousal are achieved. This is why stretching exercises are best performed after a gentle but thorough warm-up to heat the body tissues but relax the mind.

The second psychological effect of warm-up is that of mental rehearsal. Complex actions tend to be forgotten between exercise bouts. The first or second repetition of a complex action may not be as good as the fourth or fifth, when you have had time to 'get into' the movement. With skilled actions it is essential that we rehearse the movement, slowly going through a golf swing, for example, before we perform the action at full speed. This is very important with activities such as dance and martial arts which require a high degree of active flexibility.

Types of warm-up

A warm-up can either be 'passive', with the body heated from the outside, or 'active', using exercise to form the heat internally. An example of a passive warm-up is to have a sauna or hot shower. An active warm-up can be achieved through gentle jogging or using light aerobics. Both types can be effective, but are appropriate to different situations.

An active warm-up is the type normally used before exercise, while the passive warm-up is useful when stretching a muscle tightened from a previous strain. The advantage of the passive warm-up, from the point of view of injury, is that it does not require the athlete to move the injured tissues in order to create body-heat. The use of external heat can also reduce pain and muscle spasm, helping the muscle to relax and allowing the stretch to be taken further.

In addition to active and passive types, a warm-up may also be either general or specific. A general warm-up such as jogging or static cycling will affect the whole body. The effects here are mainly on the major body systems such as the heart, lungs and blood vessels. This should be followed by a specific warm-up which concentrates on the body-part and action to be used in a particular exercise. The effects now are more localised, mainly affecting body tissues used in the actual exercise and rehearsing the action to be performed.

Warm-up technique

The amount of exercise required for an effective warm-up will depend very much on a person's fitness level and the exercise to be performed in the main part of the workout. This is because changes in body temperature vary with body size, fat level and rate of body metabolism. In addition, sports differ tremendously in the demand they make on the body tissues, so a warm-up before a vigorous game of hockey would clearly need to be more extensive than one for a casual game of bowls. Equally, a top-level sprinter will require a more thorough warm-up session than a casual sportsman or woman, because the sprinter is likely to be able to push him or herself to a higher physical level.

If it is to be effective, a warm-up must be intense enough to cause mild sweating. When this happens it indicates that the inside (core) temperature of the body has increased by about 1°C. Increasing the core temperature by this amount has been shown to be the minimum requirement for bringing about the warm-up changes discussed above.

Because we are trying to raise the body temperature, it is best to perform the warm-up wearing warm clothing to keep the body-heat in. The amount of clothing needed to provide adequate insulation will depend largely on the outside temperature. Light clothing may be suitable in a warm sports-hall, but thick fleecy material with a weatherproof covering layer will be needed on the touch-line of a cold and windy pitch.

Warm-up activities should be continuous and rhythmical in nature. Gentle jogging, light aerobics, or cycling on a static bicycle in the gym are all examples of good warm-up activities. Once light sweating has begun, the major joints should be taken through their full range of movement, starting with small movements which gradually become larger. Finally, some sport-specific actions must be included in the warm-up period as a part of skill rehearsal.

A good warm-up may take 10–15 minutes, but it is time well spent. Note that we are using a warm-up before stretching rather than using stretching as part of a warm-up. This makes sense because tissues will stretch more effectively when warm. The movements we use in the warm-up to take the major joints through their range of motion are not stretching exercises as such. The warm-up movements take the joints through their full range of motion, but do not try to *increase* this range of motion as stretching exercises would.

Warm-down

Just as it is vital to begin an exercise session slowly by warming up, so it is important to end it the same way by using a warm-down or cool-down. The warm-down period has a number of important effects. First, during intense exercise the heartbeat increases, and the beating of the heart is actually helped by the contraction of the exercising limb muscles. As these muscles contract they squeeze the blood vessels which travel through them, thus helping the blood to return to the heart. If an athlete stops exercising suddenly, the limb muscles no longer pump the blood vessels and help the heart. The demand placed on the heart is increased and the pulse will actually get faster although exercise has stopped.

An effective warm-down can also reduce muscle ache. This is caused partly by lactic acid formation, and partly through tiny muscle tears which occur during very hard training. The result is that hard training causes local swelling within a muscle, giving *delayed onset muscle soreness* (DOMS). Here you feel fine the day after a workout, but the day after this you feel stiff. To reduce these effects you should perform a warm-down using similar exercises to those chosen for the warm-up, gradually lowering the exercise intensity until resting levels are reached. It is interesting to note that stretching exercises may be used to reduce muscle pain which occurs after intensive strength training.

Finally, shake your muscles to loosen and relax them, and take a warm shower to flush fresh blood through them and aid recovery. Because blood is still needed in the muscles after exercise in order to aid recovery, you should not eat a large meal immediately. If you feel hungry and in need of an 'energy boost' eat a small amount of sweet, high-carbohydrate food such as a banana or a piece of toast and honey.

Overload

To achieve a training effect, the body must be exposed to a physical stress which is greater than that encountered in every-day living. If this is done the body is said to be *overloaded*, and the body tissues will change or 'adapt' as a result.

As fitness improves, exercise must get harder so that the body continues to be taxed to the same degree. The body has adapted to the training load, and so further improvement will only occur if the training intensity is increased.

In addition to how hard an exercise is (intensity), the training must be continued for long enough (duration). High-intensity training which is too brief may not allow enough time for the body to adapt. How often the training is carried out (frequency) is also important. Training is a stimulus which causes a physical change in the body. This change will take time to occur, and so adequate recovery must be allowed between training sessions.

When training for stamina the intensity of exercise may be determined by the pulse rate, and when training for strength by the weight lifted. The intensity of flexibility training may be assessed by the range of movement and how long the stretch is held.

Training effects

We have seen that an overload on body tissue gives a training effect. This effect is largely reversible, however. If training stops, the benefits achieved for each fitness component will be lost and 'detraining' will occur.

In just 20 days of total rest, stamina reduces by 25% – a loss of about 1% per day. Strength reduction is even greater, with average losses over the same period of 35%. Muscles which have become more flexible with training will slowly tighten again, and muscle imbalance may occur if some muscles tighten more quickly than others (see page 38). Skill-based components including sports technique, balance and co-ordination last longer, but will gradually degrade with time. The principle is clear – 'use it or lose it'!

Exercise has immediate, short-term and long-term effects. The immediate effects are the body's responses to exercise. These are brought about by increased metabolism and include higher heart and breathing rates, changes in blood flow, increased body temperature, and chemical alterations to enzymes within the working muscles. When exercise stops, the body tries to reduce its metabolic rate to resting levels once more and the short-term training effects due to recovery become apparent. Body temperature has increased, so sweating continues to try to cool the tissues. Energy has been used and must be replaced, so breathing rate and heart rate remain high. Waste products have been formed as energy was 'burnt', and these wastes must be eliminated.

Long-term changes are the cumulative effects of exercise, reflecting the body's adaptation to training. Intense training stresses the body. Over time, the body learns from this and changes so that the next training bout will not stress it as much.

If a training session is not intense enough, it will not stress the body sufficiently and no adaptation will occur. However, if it is too intense the body cannot cope and injury may result. Following training, time must be allowed for the body to change and adapt, so rest for recovery from exercise is vital.

Specificity

Over a period of time, the demands placed on the body during exercise cause the body to change. With stretching, the muscles get more flexible; with weight training they get stronger; and with running, stamina improves. These changes are the adaptations to exercise and will closely match the type of demand placed on the body. For example, running marathons will improve aerobic endurance, while sprinting will build anaerobic power. If we wanted to improve our distance-running ability there would be little point in using sprint training, because the body adaptation which would occur would not be the one we want.

This example illustrates an important principle, that of *training specificity*. We can say that all training follows the SAID principle, standing for 'specific adaptation to imposed demand'. Put simply, this dictates that the change which takes place in the body (the adaptation) will closely resemble (be specific to) the type of training used (the imposed demand).

Applying this principle to stretching means that when choosing stretching exercises to improve sports performance we must match the range of motion, the muscles stretched, and the muscle balance around a joint to similar actions in the desired sport. For example, if a soccer player wants stretching exercises, these can be designed for the muscles used in kicking. The exercises should take account of any tightness a player may already have, and the stretching programme should be individually designed. Also, stretching should be applied as part of a general training programme, so that increases in flexibility are matched by strength improvements which enable the player to control the new range of motion which he or she has gained.

Components of fitness

It is generally accepted that two types of fitness exist: health related and task (performance) related. These include various components which can be described as 'S' factors for convenience (*see* table 3). Health-related fitness includes components which are considered to be beneficial to health. In this context the term *stamina* is used to encompass both heart–lung fitness and muscle endurance. This fitness component is important to the health of the heart and circulatory system. *Suppleness* (flexibility) and *strength* are concerned with the health of the musculo-skeletal system, and are important in injury prevention.

Table 3   The 'S' factors of fitness

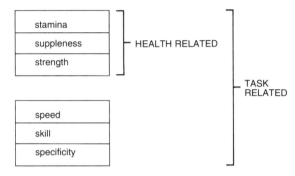

These three components are all essential to sports performance, but in addition *speed* and *skilled action* are required. Speed involves rapid muscle contraction and the elastic abilities of the muscle (*see* page 29) and is important for explosive events. Skill includes the skills needed for a particular sport, as well as general skills such as balance and co-ordination.

Injury will be more likely if the fitness components become unbalanced. For example, an inexperienced bodybuilder may have excessive strength in comparison with their flexibility, making muscle pulls more likely. A poorly trained distance runner may have a lot of stamina to protect the heart, but very little strength or flexibility, leaving the joints open to injury. Many keep-fit enthusiasts see themselves as 'very fit' because they may be strong and supple and have plenty of stamina. But endless hours spent working on gym machines will do little to improve skill, and athletes can be left clumsy with poor balance and co-ordination ability. So the message is clear: an overall training programme must work on **all** the fitness components if it is to be totally effective.

CHAPTER 5

Stretching concepts

Factors limiting flexibility

What stops a joint moving through an infinite range of motion? We need to look at two areas to explain this: external (environmental) factors, and internal (body) factors. One important internal factor is bone. Obviously we cannot affect the amount of bone in a joint, but we must be aware of it as a limiting factor to flexibility. After a fracture, for example, the amount of bone will increase over the fracture site. If this area is near a joint, range of motion may be reduced: in this case it would be fruitless to continue a stretching programme to this region. Equally, an elderly athlete may have osteoarthrosis, a condition in which the bone surfaces of the joints become uneven and more bone is formed. Again, the bone itself may limit movement and it would be dangerous to attempt any forceful stretching manoeuvres.

Soft tissues such as tendons, ligaments, the joint capsule and the skin itself will limit movement. These tissues are *inert*, that is to say they do not contract. However, they do have elastic properties and so will stretch. Muscle is an important factor. It is contractile and its contraction is governed by a number of important reflexes. Surrounding the muscle is a connective tissue framework which will also limit movement, so a muscle may be seen as both an inert and contractile structure.

The most important external factor which affects flexibility is temperature. When warmed, the body tissues become more pliable. A thorough warm-up must therefore be performed before stretching exercises are attempted. So often, vigorous stretching exercises are performed as a warm-up, and this is very wrong. Until the tissues are warm (and an athlete starts to sweat lightly) full-range stretching exercises should not be attempted. In the same way that warm tissue is more pliable, cold tissue is stiffer.

49

Research has shown that when stretching is used after injury a greater range of motion can be achieved if the muscle is cooled with ice while holding it in its final stretched position.

Nerve stretch

Another structure, whose importance in limiting flexibility is increasingly recognised, is the nerve. The covering of the nerve and the spinal chord are continuous with each other, so stretching one will result in a tightening of the other. Flexing the spine while straightening the leg and pulling the toes up will stretch the nerves in the spine and the back of the leg maximally. To prevent too much movement and offer some protection the nerve is bound down to surrounding structures at certain points along its length. However, injury can sometimes result in swelling which sticks the nerve down at the injury site as well, causing tethering. When this happens, stretching will cause muscle spasm, pain and tingling along the path of the nerve.

If the nerve tightness has lasted for some time (in some instances this may be many years), tissue changes may occur accompanied by burning, weakness, and skin discoloration. This condition is known as *adverse neural tension* (ANT) and can occur after whiplash injuries to the neck and following low back-pain. In each case physiotherapy treatment is required to regain full-range movement, as intense sports stretching on delicate and previously injured nerves can be dangerous. If an athlete stretches and gets burning or pins and needles – either down the legs and into the toes or through the arm and into the fingers – they should see a physiotherapist and not simply continue to stretch.

Individual differences

If you ask the members of any class to perform a stretching exercise you immediately see a tremendous variation in movement. Some will be more flexible than others. Some will move into the position in a smooth and effortless way, while others stumble clumsily into the exercise. The differences reflect variations in both range of movement and skill-level between athletes.

Females are generally more flexible than males, especially around the hip and shoulder. Individuals involved in strength and power events are usually less flexible than those who use their own body-weight as resistance, such as swimmers, gymnasts, and dancers. The degree of flexibility depends also on how balanced a person's fitness programme is. Inexperienced body-builders who just train for strength and bulk are among the least flexible, while teenage girl gymnasts can be amongst the most flexible. Range of movement is also dictated by lifestyle and previous injury. Inactive individuals who get the exercise message late in life will be inflexible, and in many cases the range of movement they gain is never as great as they could have achieved had they been active all their lives. In addition, the limitation to range of movement can often be permanent, dictated by years of poor posture and faulty movement techniques.

Hormonal changes will affect flexibility, especially in females. During pregnancy, and to a lesser extent during menstruation, relaxin hormone is released into the bloodstream. This, together with progesterone and oestrogen, has the effect of relaxing the pelvic ligaments especially, and making the joint between the base of the spine and the pelvis (the sacroiliac joint) more mobile. The effects of hormone changes may remain for as long as six months after pregnancy, so during this time the athlete is at risk from rapid end-range stretching exercises.

Previous injuries can leave a reduced range of movement as the only outward sign that problems have occurred. Athletes with a history of low back-pain will often be tight in the lower spine and hamstring muscles, while those with shoulder problems may be left with limited shoulder rotation movements. In cases where an athlete's flexibility is asymmetrical (greater on one side of the body than the other) a flexibility programme must aim to restore symmetry and not just increase range of movement.

Flexibility and body type

Each of us has a different type of body. Some are fatter, some are thinner, and some are more or less muscled. The degree to which we differ can be partially explained by our 'body type' or 'somatotype'. Three extreme body types are recognised: endomorphs (fatter); mesomorphs (muscular); and ectomorphs (thinner) (see fig. 25).

Endomorphs have rounder physiques and they tend to put on and store fat. They have a 'pear drop' appearance with the abdomen being as large or larger than the chest – the typical 'Billy Bunter' character. Mesomorphs have more bone and muscle development. Their bodies are made for strenuous physical activity, and individuals of this type tend to be heavily muscled. The chest is broad, and the shoulders are wider than the waist

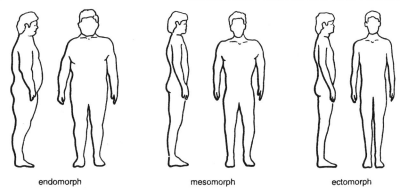

endomorph   mesomorph   ectomorph

Fig. 25 *Somatotypes – the three estreme body types*

– the 'Tarzan' type. Ectomorphs have long delicate limbs – the traditional 'bean-poles'.

In reality, few people have physiques which fall firmly into just one of these categories. We are all a mixture of the three extremes. By taking height, weight, bone size, limb girth and body-fat measurements, an individual can be given a score indicating the proportion of each body-type component present in their physiques.

Scores range from 1 to 7, and are presented in the order endomorph/mesomorph/ectomorph. Thus a highly endomorphic individual would score 7/1/1 and a high mesomorph 1/7/1. The somatotype rating can be illustrated graphically so that somatotype averages for different sports can be compared (*see* fig. 26). We can see, for example, that both gymnasts and ice hockey players have a high degree of mesomorphy, but that the hockey players have a greater tendency to endomorphy than do the gymnasts. Bodybuilders are highly mesomorphic, as we would expect. Both ballet dancers and swimmers are roughly

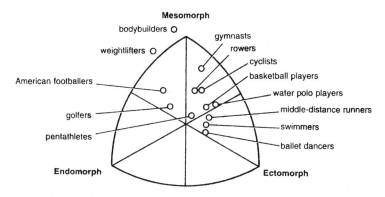

Fig. 26 *Elite athlete somatotypes*

average on all scores, possibly reflecting the fact that these athletes use their own body-weight as resistance.

Flexibility methods

We have seen that range of motion can be limited by both inert structures and by the contractile portion of the muscle. Muscle reflexes are important when trying to stretch muscles, while an adequate warm-up is needed to make the tissues more pliable before we stretch. Following a warm-up, the body should be kept warm throughout the stretching period by using warm, loose-fitting clothing such as jog bottoms and a sweat shirt.

Five methods of flexibility training are generally used: *static*, *active*, *ballistic*, and two PNF methods.

Static stretching involves taking a limb to the point at which tightness is felt, and holding this position. This is the sort of flexibility used in yoga, for example. As the position is held, the inert structures gradually elongate, while the muscle reflexes detect tension in the muscle tendon and gradually allow the muscle to relax. This is a particularly safe method of stretching, but because the position is held for up to 30 seconds the starting position chosen for the exercise must be comfortable and well supported. Lying and sitting on a mat are good starting positions, but kneeling and single leg standing are not. Once the position is achieved, concentrating on breathing out and 'sighing' can allow the muscle to relax further. When the stretch is released the muscle tension must come off slowly without allowing the tissues to 'spring' back.

Active stretching involves an active contraction (isometric or concentric) of one muscle to full inner range, requiring the antagonist to stretch fully to outer range. This is the type of stretching required in most sports, developing flexibility and strength at the same time. In addition it requires good control and so enhances skill. This type of flexibility is most common in ballet and martial arts. An example is standing holding on to a wall-bar for support and actively flexing the hip slowly to its maximum range while keeping the knee locked.

Ballistic stretching involves repeated small bounces at the end of the range of movement. Two factors are important here. First, where the whole body or trunk are used, the weight of the body moving at speed will build up momentum. The energy contained within the momentum can make it impossible to stop the movement soon enough. Tissues are overstretched, and repeated small tears can occur called microtrauma. Over the years this can cause a build-up of scar tissue, altering the mechanics of a joint. Second, the stretch reflex dictates that a rapid stretch will cause muscles to contract and tighten. Instead of increasing range of motion, the range may then actually reduce. It becomes obvious that this type of stretching is both dangerous and ineffective in most situations.

However, ballistic stretching can have an important role when carried out under the supervision of a physiotherapist after injury. The reason for this is that many sports, such as martial arts, actually involve full-range actions and a high degree of flexibility. If the actions are performed slowly they are active flexibility actions, but when performed explosively – as they often are competitively – they become ballistic actions. The athlete practising such sports does not get injured each time he kicks simply because he has trained his body to re-set the stretch reflex so that it does not occur at the speed at which he is kicking.

If the athlete should suffer an injury, however, he must regain lost strength and flexibility and gradually reintroduce ballistic flexibility before he attempts competitive sport once more. This must be done in a highly controlled and supervised manner. Initially only mid-range movements are used; gradually the range of motion is increased over many training sessions. It must be emphasised that full static, active, and PNF flexibility and full strength and power should be regained before any ballistic actions are used. The danger comes when inexperienced athletes try to copy a person who has been training with this type of action for many years. The body of the inexperienced athlete has not had time to adapt itself to these highly specialised actions and so injury is the frequent outcome.

PNF (standing for 'proprioceptive neuromuscular facilitation') is a method adapted from physiotherapy treatment of patients who have had strokes. It involves a series of movements designed to get the maximum out of a muscle by using primitive muscle reflexes. The first technique is called *contract–relax* (CR). With this method the athlete must first contract the muscle to be stretched and hold the contraction for 10–20 seconds. During this period the golgi tendon organs will register the tension build-up and cause autogenic inhibition, allowing an increased range of motion to be achieved. Because the muscle is tensed isometrically this technique is also called *post-isometric relaxation* (PIR).

The other method of PNF stretching is called CRAC (contract–relax–agonist–contract). This consists of the contract–relax method first, but goes further to use the fact that when one muscle contracts, its opposing neighbour (the antagonist) must relax. This reflex, called *reciprocal innervation*, allows us to stretch still further. To perform the CRAC method the muscle to be stretched is first contracted and held for 20 seconds. This muscle is then relaxed, a brief pause is allowed, and then the opposing muscle is contracted to pull further into the stretched position. This has the added benefit of strengthening the muscle group which controls the range of motion, but can be difficult for some athletes to practise unsupervised.

All static and PNF stretching can be illustrated by a straight-leg-raise movement to stretch the hamstrings (*see* page 90). The athlete lies on a mat and flexes the hip, keeping the knee locked. A training partner then presses the leg further into flexion and holds the new position to perform a static stretch. If the athlete now presses the leg down on to the shoulder of their training partner, holds the hamstrings tight and then relaxes before the stretch is applied, he is applying CR. If, while the stretch is being applied, the athlete pulls the straight leg into further flexion, trying to help their training partner, he is using CRAC.

Partner work

Stretching can be done individually, but is sometimes more effective when performed with a partner. On the plus side, motivation is better; but on the minus side the situation is less controlled because two people are involved.

In each case a stable starting position must be chosen, with no chance of either person falling and violently increasing the stretch. The two partners act as one unit, and so their combined mass has a single base of support and line of gravity (*see* page 6). The base of support must therefore be larger than it would be for a single person. The person applying the stretch must move into a comfortable position which they can easily maintain, rather than into an awkward position which places them off-balance or is uncomfortable (thus making them continuously readjust their position).

The person who is being stretched must control the range of motion by giving continuous feedback. The techniques used must be fully explained to both partners, and they must both agree on the amount of pressure and length of hold which will be used. Initially, only minimal pressure should be used to increase the stretch. Pressure should not be exerted over a joint or an area of bone which may be painful – for example, the kneecap.

If partner activities are applied in a group exercise situation they must be practised under the supervision of an experienced and skilled instructor. Close supervision of individuals in the group is essential, especially when dealing with young or inexperienced athletes. When teaching partner-work to adolescents, they should be matched for body size and degree of flexibility.

Use of apparatus

Any form of training requires that the body is overloaded sufficiently to cause an adaptation. In the case of stretching exercises the overload is to increase the range of motion and hold the position. This is normally achieved manually, but apparatus may be used. Most commonly a towel or belt is used to support the part of the body being stretched and to allow greater relaxation. For example, where a subject is quite inflexible, hamstring stretches (see page 75) can sometimes be easier if a towel is placed around the foot. Belts and pads may be used to keep the spine straight when hip exercises are used and there is a tendency to allow the spine to round, increasing lumbar stress.

Various machines are available to facilitate adductor stretches in the hope of achieving the classic 'splits' position. These are normally hydraulic or ratchet devices which force the legs further into abduction. From the point of view of safety, the amount of force used and its point of application are of paramount importance. Forcing the hips into an abducted position can place an excessive stress on the hip tissues. Applying this force below the knee can stress the medial ligament of the knee by imposing an inward (valgus) stress on these structures.

Continuous passive motion (CPM) machines have been used in a hospital setting for a number of years, and these are now being seen in the sporting context. The machines are electrically powered, and move the joints through a specified range for a set period. The amount of force available makes it essential that these machines are used only under the direct supervision of a physiotherapist.

Developing agility

We have seen that fitness is composed of a number of components. Of these, flexibility is only one – the ability to obtain a range of motion about a joint. Agility by comparison is the ability to use and control this range of motion. For this reason, good agility requires a number of fitness components: flexibility, strength, muscle endurance, skill, and speed. Agility is thus fundamental to good sports performance.

Agility exercises involve controlled movements through a full range of motion, and may be used individually or in a circuit training format. Examples include movements from dance, ballet, aerobics and gymnastics, together with sport-specific actions requiring a high degree of agility.

Starting positions

The starting position for any stretching exercise is important both in terms of safety and effectiveness. It must allow free movement of the part of the body that is to be stretched, and it must be stable. An unstable position can cause an athlete to lose balance and therefore lose control of a movement, placing excessive strain on the tissues being stretched. In addition, positions which are uncomfortable do not allow athletes to relax completely, and excessive tension in a muscle is not conducive to effective stretching. Furthermore, some athletes may have medical conditions which dictate that certain starting positions are unsuitable if they place excessive or unbalanced stress on a weakened part of the body. Table 4 shows a variety of common starting positions with points to note and suggested modifications.

Table 4   Starting positions

Starting position	Points to note	Modifications
Standing	Athlete must stand in an erect and balanced posture. Common errors are to stand in a slumped or round-shouldered posture which does not allow correct spinal movement. With the feet together the position is unstable, especially if an athlete has poor balance. The body-weight must be taken equally through both legs.	Standing with feet apart (stride standing), or with one foot in front of the other (walk standing), facing the direction of movement. Improve stability further by holding on to an object (support standing).
'Walk standing' (one foot in front of the other). 'Step standing' (one foot up on a step)	Both positions are more stable than standing alone, but excessive stress may be placed on the knee if leg alignment is not correct. Ensure that the knee passes directly over the middle of the foot on the leading leg.	Use the thigh of the leading leg to lean on for support.
Supine lying	If the hip flexors are tight the pelvis may be tilted forwards, increasing the lumbar lordosis and placing pressure on the lumbar spine (see page 64). In athletes who have little body fat and prominent pelvic bones, pressure from a hard floor on body prominences can be painful. Some elderly subjects find lying makes breathing difficult for them, and some with arthritis of the neck joints find lying without a pillow causes dizziness and nausea.	Always lie on a padded mat. Use a rolled towel beneath the lower spine for support. Raise the neck on a small pillow or folded towel for elderly subjects. Bend the knees (crook lying) to relax the hip flexors and reduce pressure on the lumbar spine.
Prone lying	Athlete must turn the head to one side to be able to breath freely, and this can place excessive stress on the neck if the position is held. Pressure over prominent pelvic bones can be painful, and male subjects may find testicular compression occurs. Those with patellar pain find compression on a hard surface extremely painful.	Always use a well-padded mat, and encourage male subjects to press testicles away from compression from the pubic bone. Place a rolled towel below the forehead to enable the subject to breathe freely without compressing the nose. Bend the knees and place a rolled towel beneath the ankles.
Sitting	When the hips are flexed further than 45°, tightness in the hip tissues begins to tilt the pelvis and flatten the spine. Eventually the spine may round, giving back-pain after prolonged periods. Holding the head too far forwards places stress on the neck and shoulder muscles.	Encourage athlete to 'sit tall' and avoid slumping. Sit with knees apart to allow pelvis to tilt freely and maintain the lumbar lordosis.
Kneeling	Pressure on the front of the knee is very painful. Kneeling on all fours (prone kneeling) may place stress on the wrist. Kneeling on the knees only (high kneeling) places increased stress on the patella and can be unstable.	Use a well-padded mat. Ensure that the knees are shoulder-width apart to aid stability. Hold on to an object when using high kneeling.

CHAPTER 6

Posture

Posture is simply the relationship (alignment) between different parts of the body. Posture is important from two standpoints. First, good posture underlies all exercise techniques. Exercises started from a basis of poor posture tend to be awkward and clumsy with unequal tension placed on some body tissues. This can eventually lead to the accumulation of stress and consequent overuse injuries. Second, postural stress in daily life overworks some tissues and underworks others, leading to an imbalance of flexibility and strength. In the short term this imbalance gives rise to postural pain; but in the long term, because joints are pulled out of alignment, altered joint mechanics can lead to the development of osteoarthritis.

Posture is maintained by both muscles and non-contractile tissues. A good posture is one in which the different parts of the body are correctly aligned, thus placing the minimum amount of stress on the body tissues. A good posture requires little muscle activity, so it is more relaxed and needs less energy to maintain it. At the same time, joint structures are not over-stretched or shortened so much that they cause strain. In both of these cases a good posture is one which is balanced.

Two types of posture are important. Static posture is that seen at rest, while dynamic posture is that of motion – the type of body position a person takes up when moving. Static posture may be assessed by close inspection of the body, but the study of dynamic posture requires in-depth training, and often the use of advanced laboratory facilities.

A number of factors interact to create a person's static posture. Body type (see page 51) and genetic make-up are important, as are strength and flexibility. In addition, the way a person sees themselves (their body image) and the mental state of an individual will affect posture.

An individual cannot easily alter their bony make-up, so the posture with which they were genetically endowed is largely permanent unless surgically changed. Children who have particular spinal deformities, for example, often require a number of complex operations to straighten the spine. Similarly bone or skeletal 'frame size' is constant for an individual, so a stretching programme must take this into account.

The important factor in the development of both flexibility and strength is *symmetry*. An unequal development of either of these two elements can pull the body out of alignment and so cause postural faults. We have seen in chapter 3 (pp. 26–39) that there is an intimate link between flexibility and strength in the muscle imbalance process. A tight muscle will have increased tone, and through reciprocal innervation this will inhibit the strength of its antagonist. In any movement a number of muscles will contract in a specific sequence. When one muscle of a group is tight, however, it will contract first – out of sequence – and will make the movement appear clumsy. We say that the inhibited muscle is suffering from 'pseudoparesis' and that the tight muscle when it contracts first is 'dominant'.

Assessment of standing posture

From behind

When the body is viewed from behind, with the feet 3 inches apart, a vertical line should divide it into two equal halves. The pelvic rims (anterior superior iliac spines) should be in the same horizontal plane, and the pubis and pelvic rims should be in the same vertical plane. The athlete's posture is compared to the score-chart (*see* table 5). Body landmarks are compared for horizontal level on the right and left sides of the body, and include the knee creases, buttock creases, pelvic rim, angle of the shoulder blades, upper arm bones, ears, and skull protuberances. In addition, the alignment of the spinous processes and rib angles is observed. The distance between the arms and the trunk (keyhole), skin creases, and unequal muscle bulk are indicators of asymmetrical posture. Slight side bending of the spine (scoliosis) becomes more noticeable when the athlete bends forwards (Adam's position) and a marked hump is seen over the twisted ribs.

Table 5   Assessment of standing position from behind

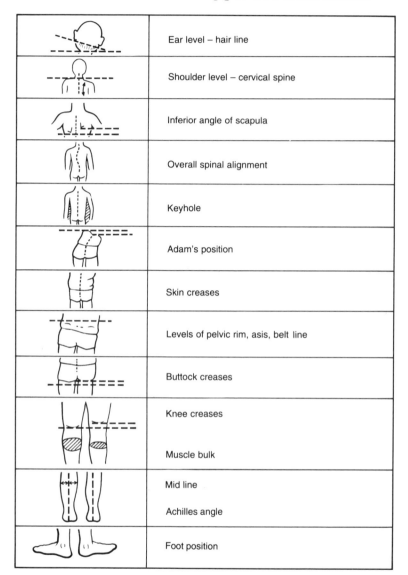

	Ear level – hair line
	Shoulder level – cervical spine
	Inferior angle of scapula
	Overall spinal alignment
	Keyhole
	Adam's position
	Skin creases
	Levels of pelvic rim, asis, belt line
	Buttock creases
	Knee creases Muscle bulk
	Mid line Achilles angle
	Foot position

From the side

Standing posture is assessed by comparing it to a plumb-line or vertical line on a wall (*see* fig. 27). The line begins just in front of the outer ankle bone (lateral malleolus). In an ideal posture this line should pass just in front of the midline of the knee, and then through the hip, lumbar vertebrae, shoulder joint, cervical vertebrae, and the lobe of the ear. In this case the chest is the furthest point forwards, and the buttocks are the furthest backwards. The posture is balanced and requires little muscle activity to maintain. When the body moves away from the plumb-line, stress is placed on the body tissues and muscles have to work harder to maintain the unbalanced body position.

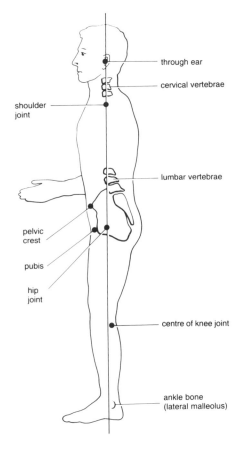

through ear

cervical vertebrae

shoulder joint

lumbar vertebrae

pelvic crest

pubis

hip joint

centre of knee joint

ankle bone (lateral malleolus)

Fig. 27   Posture plumbline

Postural faults and correction

Common postural faults identified from behind which require stretching include tightness of the upper trapezius which pulls the neck to one side, tightness of one set of spinal muscles which pulls the spine to one side, and unequal development of muscles requiring strengthening exercises. Once stretching exercises have been performed to return the muscles to their correct resting length, weight training may be needed to selectively re-strengthen the postural muscles. For further reading *see Weight Training: Principles and Practice* by C. M. Norris (A&C Black, 1993).

Common postural faults viewed from the side include the round-shouldered posture (kyphotic), the sway-back posture, the flat-back posture and the hollow-back (lordotic) posture – *see* fig. 28.

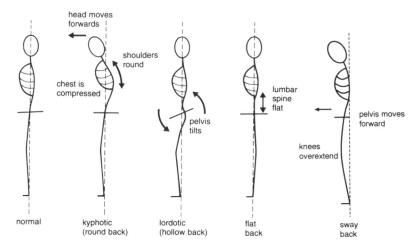

Fig. 28   Postural faults viewed from the side

Hollow-back posture

The lower part of the back (the lumbar spine) should normally be slightly hollow. This curve (the lumbar lordosis) is greatly affected by the tilt of the pelvis. The pelvis is balanced like a see-saw on the hip-joints, and is controlled by the abdominal, spinal and hip muscles and the ligaments which surround these areas. The abdominal muscles, working together with the gluteals and hamstrings, will tilt the pelvis backwards and flatten the lower spine, while the hip flexors and spinal extensors will tilt the pelvis forwards and increase the lumbar curve.

In many cases an imbalance of these muscles exists, known as the *pelvic crossed syndrome* (PCS). Here we see a combination of excessive length and weakness in the abdominal muscles and gluteals (sagging) and tightness in the spinal extensors and iliopsoas (*see* fig. 29). The pelvis is seen to tip forwards, pulling the lumbar spine into an increased curvature or lordosis. This in turn causes stress to the small facet joints deep within the lumbar spine. This is the classic 'beer belly' posture, also seen after pregnancy and as a result of abdominal surgery.

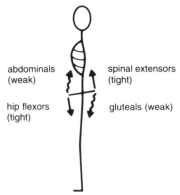

abdominals
(weak)

spinal extensors
(tight)

hip flexors
(tight)

gluteals (weak)

Fig. 29   *The pelvic crossed syndrome (PCS)*

The weakness of the gluteal muscles has an important bearing on walking and running. Normally, as we take a step and the hip moves into extension, the gluteal muscles contract powerfully to push the body forwards. However, in PCS these muscles are weak and so are unable to propel the body correctly. To compensate for this, the hamstring muscles contract in an attempt to do the work of the gluteals (the hamstrings eventually becoming tight themselves). Because the hamstrings are not as strong as the gluteals, the action of hip extension is weaker. The body tries to make up for this by extending the lumbar spine instead of the hip, and again stress is placed on this region. The appearance now when running, stepping and walking is of a 'duck waddle' around the pelvic region.

To correct this syndrome it is fruitless to simply strengthen the gluteal muscles alone, because the imbalance affects all the hip muscles. Instead we must focus our attention first on stretching the tight muscles which are inhibiting the movement. In the case of PCS we must stretch the iliopsoas and hamstrings (*see* table 6(d/e)). Once this has been achieved, both the gluteals and the lower abdominal muscles must be re-strengthened to correct the pelvic tilt. It is important to work the abdominals in their inner range to shorten rather than simply strengthen the muscles.

Kyphotic posture

An imbalance pattern also exists around the shoulder girdle, known as the *upper crossed syndrome* (UCS). Here the upper trapezius, levator scapulae and pectoral muscles are tight, while the deep neck flexors and the lower scapular stabilisers (serratus anterior and lower trapezius) are inhibited and weak. The abnormal posture seen here is one in which the head is held

Table 6 Stretching exercises for posture

PROBLEM	EXERCISE	
Head appears to be held forwards , poking chin		Chin tuck
Tight band from neck to shoulder (upper trapezius). Head appears tilted to one side		Side bend
Round shoulders		'pec stretch'
Tight hip flexors		Iliopsoas
Tight hamstrings		Hamstrings
Flat low back		Low back
Tight back when bending forwards		Low back

forwards (poking chin) and the normal curve in the neck is flattened out. The head posture places stress on the neck tissues and frequent headaches can result. The shoulders are rounded and the scapulae move further apart. In some cases the scapulae can be seen standing prominent under the skin (winging). Tightness in the trapezius and levator scapulae is commonly seen as a straightening of the neck/shoulder line, where the muscles stand out like tight cords (see fig. 30). This posture is frequently seen in those who spend many hours slumped over a desk and do little exercise in their spare time.

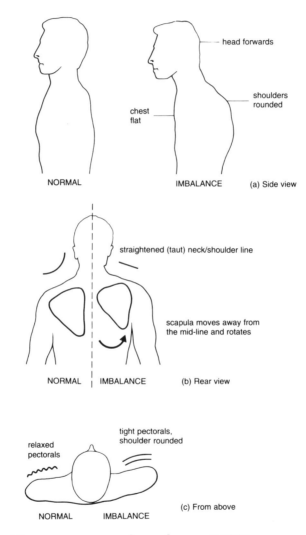

Fig. 30   *The upper crossed syndrome (UCS)*

The altered muscular control of the scapulae causes them to twist slightly so that the shoulder socket (glenoid fossa) faces more vertically than normal. This means that the shoulder muscles must work harder to stop the joint from dislocating, and this additional work can give rise to a painful 'frozen shoulder' over time.

Although the shoulder girdle is a separate structure from the thoracic spine, the shoulder posture in UCS pulls the thoracic spine into excessive flexion, forcing the ribs together and making breathing more difficult. In some cases the thoracic vertebrae soften and develop incorrectly, a condition called Scheurmanns disease which requires specialist treatment. In this case, the shoulder posture results from the spinal posture rather than the other way round.

Where the kyphotic posture is created by tissue tightness alone, stretching is called for. Stretching is aimed at the neck (see table 6(a)), the levator scapulae and upper trapezius (see table 6(b)), and the pectoral and anterior deltoid muscles (see table 6(c)). The deep neck flexors and shoulder stabilisers are strengthened.

In many cases the lordotic posture and the kyphotic posture may occur together (kypho-lordosis). This is because the increase in the lumbar lordosis results in an increased kyphosis to compensate and bring the body-weight back over the plumb-line. If this is the case, exercise therapy must be aimed at both areas.

Sway-back posture

In a sway-back posture the whole pelvis moves forwards and the hips are forced into extension. While the pelvic tilt remains the same, the thorax flexes and the lumbar lordosis is increased. This stresses the hip ligaments, and the ligaments on the front of the lower spine and behind the thoracic spine.

Comparing normal and sway-back postures (see fig. 31) we can see that in the case of normal posture the furthest point forwards is the chest and the furthest backwards is the buttocks. In the case of sway-back posture the furthest point forwards is the abdomen and the furthest back is the thoracic spine. In the normal posture the lumbar curve is gently hollow along the whole length of the lumbar spine. In the sway-back, the hollow is sharp and more pronounced in the lower area. Finally, in the normal posture the spine and leg are close to the plumb-line, but in the sway-back the spine and leg form a curve.

The sway-back tends to be a temporary 'slouching' posture, frequently seen in adolescents as they suddenly start to grow tall and 'shoot up'. However, it is still a cause of pain when held for longer periods. Correction involves tucking the chin in and

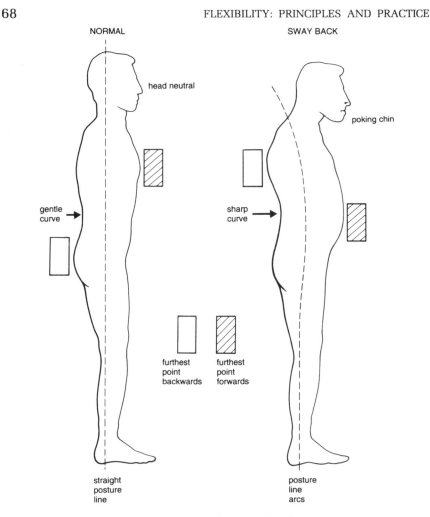

Fig. 31   Comparing normal and sway-back postures

lengthening the spine as though you were a puppet on a rope hanging from the ceiling. In addition the chest should move forwards while the pelvis remains still. This is easiest to learn by standing in front of a table and imagining the pelvis and chest as two child's building blocks sliding on top of each other (*see* fig. 32). The hips should not touch the table, and the chest should slide forwards as one unit, without altering spinal alignment.

Flat-back posture

The flat-back posture shows a markedly reduced lumbar lordosis, and is commonly seen following back-pain where a person has rested in bed. The individual is unable to move the spine

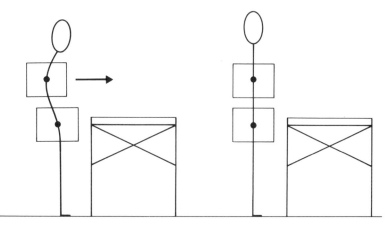

Fig. 32   Correcting the sway-back posture

correctly and most of the structures around it are stiff and sore. Stiffness may limit either flexion or extension, and the spine becomes almost fixed in a flat-back position. Stretching can help to alleviate the pain from this condition as the lost flexibility is gradually regained. The stretches should feel slightly uncomfortable because they are working on very tight structures. However, they should not give back-pain. If they do, exercise should only be carried out under the supervision of a physiotherapist.

With the flat-back posture the spine is gradually stretched into extension (*see* table 6(f)). Where forward bending is also limited, flexion stretches may be performed using the hips for leverage (*see* table 6(g)). In each case the movement is gently encouraged rather than being vigorously forced.

Postural faults in the lower limb

Postural faults in the foot and leg can be detrimental to knee health, and stretching can help to alleviate them. We have seen that imbalance between the various hip and lumbar spine muscles can alter the way in which the hip is extended when walking and running. A further imbalance pattern also exists between the hip abductor and adductor muscles. The adductors show a tendency to tighten, and this in turn inhibits the hip abductors. The abductor muscles are important stabilisers of the pelvis as we lift one leg from the ground in walking, stepping and running. As we lift the leg, the abductor muscles of the leg on the ground work hard to prevent the pelvis from dipping down. If these muscles are inhibited and weak, the pelvis dips causing a sideways 'duck waddle' (see fig. 33), most noticeable when performing step aerobics.

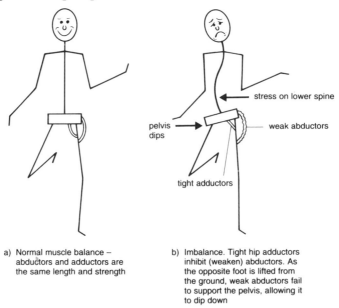

a) Normal muscle balance –
abductors and adductors are
the same length and strength

b) Imbalance. Tight hip adductors
inhibit (weaken) abductors. As
the opposite foot is lifted from
the ground, weak abductors fail
to support the pelvis, allowing it
to dip down

Fig. 33   Weak hip abductors altering the stepping gait

We saw that when the hip extensors are weak the hamstring muscles work by substitution in the PCS, and in so doing they become tight. The same happens when the hip abductors are weak. Now, the tensor fascia lata muscle works instead. This muscle attaches into a band of tissue travelling down the side of the leg, called the ilio tibial tract (ITB). The ITB in turn has a connection into the side of the kneecap. Because the tensor fascia lata is having to work too hard to cover up for the weakened hip abductors, it tightens the ITB and pulls the kneecap outwards as weight is taken on one leg. This is a very common cause of a painful kneecap, so often seen in sport.

The action now is clear. First we must stretch the tight hip adductors. Then, if the condition has been present for some time, the ITB will be tight and will need to be stretched by a physiotherapist.

PART TWO

Practical Application

CHAPTER 7

The exercises

In this section we look at a variety of stretching exercises. The list is by no means exhaustive but describes the most useful exercises for sport. Before performing any of the movements make sure that you are thoroughly warmed up. You should be sweating lightly and wrapped in loose-fitting clothing to maintain body-heat. Each movement should be performed in a slow, controlled manner with no bouncing or bobbing actions. Hold the stretched position for 10–20 seconds and then slowly release. You should feel a comfortable stretch, but no pain.

For clarity, the descriptions refer to the right-hand side of the body, but obviously the left side may be stretched just as easily. Each stretch is described in terms of major muscles stretched, starting position, technique, variations, and points to note. Where relevant, partner stretches are added.

Major muscle(s) stretched

This refers only to the main training effect of the stretch. Other parts of the body will be used, but their involvement will normally be secondary. Muscles and joint structures will both be stretched: for this reason, it is important to determine if excessive strain is being placed on a joint when you are actually trying to stretch a muscle. Often, simply changing the starting position will reduce joint stress but maintain the effectiveness of the stretch on the muscle (see page 58).

Starting position

In the starting position you should be comfortable and well supported. If you are unstable, the danger is that the movement may be uncontrolled and you could fall, suddenly increasing the

73

stretch and causing injury. Take time to make yourself comfortable so you do not need to readjust your posture once you have started the stretch.

Technique

Before you start to stretch, re-read pages 53 to 55 which describe the different types of stretching. Initially it will probably be best for you to apply static stretching. As you gain flexibility you should progress to PNF stretches and finally active stretching to maintain strength, balance and co-ordination. The stretch should be applied as you exhale to aid relaxation.

Remember, if you become too flexible (hyperflexible) you may not have enough strength in the muscles around your joints to support them throughout their whole range of motion. In this case your joints may become unstable and open to injury. Always balance any improvements in flexibility with improvements in the other fitness components (see page 47), especially strength.

Variations

Variations of exercises are included because these prevent you from getting stale. In addition, two or three exercises designed to stretch exactly the same muscles will each stress the body in slightly different ways. These different stresses reduce the likelihood of developing overuse injuries. You will have preferences for certain exercises, and some will suit you more than others, depending on your body-size and make-up. This is fine, and serves to individualise your stretching programme.

Partner stretch

Partner stretches are described individually in exercises 40 to 45. Some stretches are easily modified into partner stretches, and these modifications are described in conjunction with the general exercise details. Before performing partner stretches you should re-read pages 55 to 56.

Points to note

This section explains any idiosyncrasies pertaining to a particular exercise, and is important because these are sometimes concerned with safety factors and injury prevention. You may like to make a note of any points you find relevant to your own training style after reading this section.

Exercise 1

AREAS STRETCHED: Hamstrings, spinal extensors

STARTING POSITION: Begin with the right leg straight, the left comfortably bent at the knee and hip. The legs are slightly astride and the foot is flat. Lengthen the spine to straighten it, and make sure you are sitting on your 'sitting bones' (ischial tuberosities) to tilt your pelvis forwards slightly and hollow the small of the back.

TECHNIQUE: Reach forwards with your left arm, towards your right foot. As you go forwards, support your body-weight by placing your right hand above your knee.

VARIATIONS: Bending the right knee slightly will allow you to reach further forwards, and will transfer the stretch to the upper portion of the hamstrings. Pulling the toes upwards will increase the stretch on the gastrocnemius muscle of the calf. Wrapping a towel or belt around the foot will give you more leverage to pull forwards.

For those who find this exercise particularly difficult, simply hollowing the back may be a sufficient stretch. This will tilt the pelvis forwards and pull the ischial tuberosity further away from the tibia, so imparting a stretch.

PARTNER STRETCH: From the same starting position an assistant presses the spine forwards through flexion on the hip (rather than performing spinal flexion itself). Pressure is applied to the base of the spine to localise the movement to the hips, rather than to the shoulders which would encourage thoracic flexion.

Points to note: The measure of the effectiveness of this exercise is not how far you can reach towards the toes, but how much stretch is felt in the hamstrings. To reach further by bending the spine in an attempt to touch the forehead to the knee will place considerable strain on the thoracic spine (see page 129).

Short adductor stretch

Exercise 2

AREAS STRETCHED: Hip adductors other than gracilus

STARTING POSITION: Start sitting up straight with your back to a wall. Your knees should be comfortably bent with the soles of the feet together. Rest your hands lightly on top of your knees.

TECHNIQUE: Exhale and press your knees towards the floor while keeping your spine straight on the wall.

VARIATIONS: To increase the overpressure, grip your feet and press your elbows down on to your knees.

   This exercise can be performed lying down. In this case there is a tendency for the pelvis to tilt forwards and the back to hollow, so the abdominal muscles must be kept tight throughout the movement to keep the lumbar spine flat on the floor.

PARTNER STRETCH: An assistant sits in front of the athlete and applies gentle pressure over the knees. The athlete leans backwards on to the wall, keeping the spine perfectly straight.

Points to note: This exercise places considerable strain on the hip adductors. Because of the long lever provided by the femur, any bouncing actions or vigorous pair-stretching activities may pull the adductor muscle tendon away from the pubic bone, eventually causing calcification.

Hamstring stretch

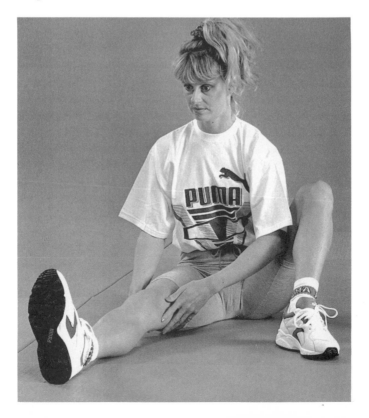

Exercise 3

AREAS STRETCHED: Hip adductors including gracilus

STARTING POSITION: Begin in a stride sitting position with your spine straight and your hands resting on the floor behind you.

TECHNIQUE: Gently press with your hands on the floor to push your body forwards, keeping your spine straight. As you push your body-weight forwards, allow your legs to open further.

VARIATIONS: Placing a small stool in front of you enables you to pull rather than push forwards into the stretch position.

PARTNER STRETCH: An assistant stands behind the athlete with his foot against the athlete's sacrum. The side of the assistant's leg is placed along the length of the athlete's spine. A folded towel may be used over the spine as padding. The assistant grasps the athlete's shoulders and presses forwards with the whole length of his leg to encourage the spine to move on the hip. At the same time he pulls back on the athlete's shoulders to keep the spine straight.

Points to note: The aim of this exercise is to tilt the pelvis forwards and pull the pubic bone back to stretch the adductors. Bending the spine does not increase the stretch on the adductors, but will overstretch the spinal tissues.

Beginning with your toes pulled towards you then pointing them as you press forwards will help the legs to move to the side slightly.

If the knees are allowed to bend, stress may be placed on the medial ligament of the knee.

Long adductor stretch with spinal support

Exercise 4

AREAS STRETCHED: Hip adductors including gracilus

STARTING POSITION: Start lying down, close to a wall, with your hips flexed to 90° and your buttocks in contact with the wall. Your legs should be straight.

TECHNIQUE: Allow your legs to lower slowly into an abducted hip position, keeping the knees locked.

VARIATIONS: This exercise may be performed away from a wall provided that the hips remain at 90° flexion throughout the movement. Cords may be used, looped round the feet and held in the hands, to support the weight of the legs.

Points to note: To ensure that the lumbar spine remains flat throughout this exercise the hips must stay flexed to 90° so that the feet, knees and hips are in a vertical line. Once the legs lower, the spine will begin to arch and considerable stress will be placed on the lumbar spine.

Long adductor stretch with wall support

Exercise 5

AREAS STRETCHED: Soleus (knee flexed), gastrocnemius (knee straight)

STARTING POSITION: Start facing a wall, with your hands touching it for stability. The right leg is back, and the foot remains flat and perpendicular to the wall.

TECHNIQUE: (i) Keeping the right leg straight, lunge forwards, increasing dorsiflexion at the ankle. (ii) Press the body-weight downwards, allowing the right leg to bend.

VARIATIONS: Altering the angle of the foot will stress the inner and outer portions of the calf and Achilles. Placing the toes on a 3 cm block will increase the stretch.

Points to note: It is important to stretch both of the calf muscles by performing each exercise on both legs.

Soleus (left) and gastrocnemius (right) stretch

Exercise 6

AREAS STRETCHED: Hamstrings and gluteals of right leg, iliopsoas and rectus femoris of left leg

STARTING POSITION: Start standing with your feet shoulder-width apart. Lunge forwards with the right leg, keeping the front foot flat and the knee and foot in line. Support your body-weight with your hands on the floor.

TECHNIQUE: Press the pelvis towards the floor to increase the flexion of the right hip. Keep the left leg relatively straight, and the knee and foot in line.

VARIATIONS: Place both arms inside the right knee, and turn the right leg outwards to gain a greater range of movement.

Points to note: If the knee is allowed to travel inwards, stress can be placed on the medial ligament of the knee. Taking the weight on the toes of the right foot makes the position less stable.

Lunge stretch

Exercise 7

AREAS STRETCHED: Internal and external rotators of the hip
STARTING POSITION: Lie prone with the knees together and flexed to 90°.
TECHNIQUE: (i) Allow the feet to travel outwards in an arc (internal rotation of the hip). (ii) Allow the feet to travel inwards in an arc (external rotation of the hip).
VARIATIONS: Using ankle weights will increase the overload of the exercise.
PARTNER STRETCH: The athlete lies on a table with an assistant at his side. The assistant places one hand at the side of the athlete's knee to prevent hip abduction, and one hand on the athlete's ankle to impose the stretching force. Inward or outward rotation is performed as above.
Points to note: Using too much weight on this exercise will stress the ligaments at the side of the knee (collateral ligaments) as the leg moves into the position of maximum stretch. Do not allow the spine to arch, or the knees to drift apart.

Hip rotator stretch

Exercise 8

AREAS STRETCHED: Adductors including gracilus

STARTING POSITION: Start with your legs astride, trunk angled forwards to the horizontal at the hips, hands on the floor to support your body-weight.

TECHNIQUE: Gently press the weight of the pelvis downwards to increase the stretch on the hip adductors.

VARIATIONS: Place the feet on towels on a polished surface to allow the feet to move outwards more easily. Rest your chest on a small stool to take your body-weight.

Points to note: This is an advanced stretch for the hip adductors. There are two areas susceptible to excessive strain, the knee and the spine. If insufficient body-weight is taken on the arms, the weight will go through the legs, forcing the knees downwards and imparting a side opening (valgus) force on the knee. This can severely stress the medial ligament of the knee.

The trunk must move on the hip to gain the horizontal body position. If the spine is allowed to flex, stress is placed on the whole spine and especially on the thoracic region.

Long adductor stretch with chest support

Exercise 9

AREAS STRETCHED: Latissimus dorsi, quadratus lumborum, oblique abdominals

STARTING POSITION: Begin standing with the feet shoulder-width apart. The left hand is by your side and resting on the left leg. The right arm is reaching overhead.

TECHNIQUE: Lean over to the left, taking your body-weight through your left arm and on to your left leg. Allow the right arm to touch the right ear.

VARIATIONS: Bending the right leg will tip the pelvis down on the right and increase the stretch on quadratus lumborum. Place your left arm on a table to take your body-weight.

Points to note: The movement should be pure lateral flexion of the spine with no forward flexion or rotation, so keep the shoulder girdle and pelvis facing forwards throughout the movement. If the body-weight is not taken on the left arm, the spine will be stressed excessively at the point of maximum stretch.

Side bend with support

Exercise 10

AREAS STRETCHED: Spine, oblique abdominals, hip abductors of right leg

STARTING POSITION: Start lying flat with your right arm abducted to 90° and your left arm by your side. The right knee is bent.

TECHNIQUE: Tuck the left hip under, and lower your right knee over your left leg and down towards the floor. Press the right knee to the floor with your left hand. Keep the shoulder and left arm on the floor.

VARIATIONS: Altering the angle of hip flexion of the right leg will change the muscle emphasis, as will straightening the right leg. If you find the stretch is too severe, lower the right knee on to a cushion. Straightening your right leg and grasping your right foot with your left hand will increase the stretch on your hamstrings and gluteals.

PARTNER STRETCH: An assistant kneels at the athlete's head and holds his right arm and shoulder on the floor throughout the stretch.

Points to note: Rotation stretches open the small facet joints in the spine and may result in clicks and pops. This is perfectly harmless and is the result of gas bubbles forming in the synovial fluid within the joint.

Spinal rotation

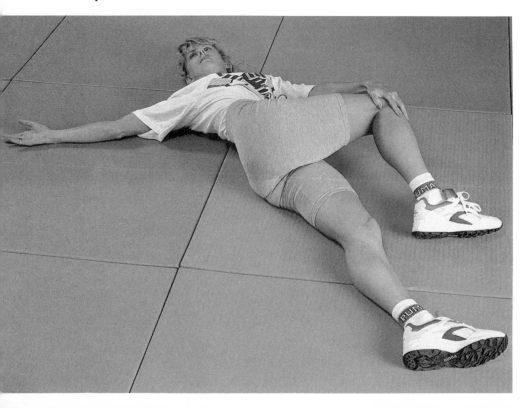

Exercise 11

AREAS STRETCHED: Lumbar spine and spinal extensors
STARTING POSITION: Lie flat and bring your knees up to your chest. Grip both legs behind your knees.
TECHNIQUE: Pull the knees in towards your chest and up to your shoulders at the same time, so your 'tailbone' (coccyx) lifts from the floor.
VARIATIONS: Pulling the knees to the right or left instead of straight up will flex the spine and slightly laterally flex and rotate it.
PARTNER STRETCH: The athlete lies on a table with the assistant to one side. The assistant places one hand beneath the athlete's sacrum and the other on his shoulder to encourage further flexion.
Points to note: This exercise will flex the spine from the bottom upwards, rather than from the top downwards as normal bending motions do. After injury, the lower two lumbar vertebrae are normally quite stiff, and this movement will focus on these without placing excessive stress on the upper spinal levels.

Passive flexion (left) and extension (right) of the lumbar spine

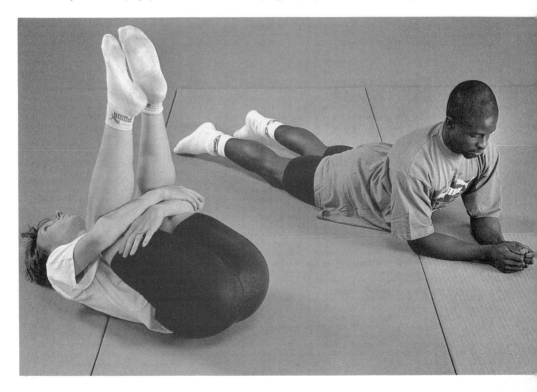

Exercise 12

AREAS STRETCHED: Lumbar spine and abdominals

STARTING POSITION: Start lying prone with your hands at the sides of your chest in the press-up position.

TECHNIQUE: Keep your hips on the floor and press-straighten your arms. Push up on to your elbows initially, and eventually use the full length of your arms.

VARIATIONS: Placing both hands by the right side of the body and looking to the right as you stretch will extend the spine and rotate and laterally flex it.

PARTNER STRETCH: An assistant may press down on the pelvis to prevent it from lifting from the floor, and to localise the movement at the lumbar spine.

Points to note: After a bout of back-pain, the normal curve (lordosis) in the lumbar region can flatten out. This exercise is very useful in restoring the lordosis and easing the pain. Performing the exercise repeatedly without maintaining the upper position will have a 'pumping' effect on the lumbar discs. This effect is exactly opposite to the stress normally imposed on the spine by repeated bending movements encountered in daily activities. The movement can therefore be used to reduce the risk of back-pain which may develop through the build-up of flexion stresses on the lumbar spine.

Passive flexion (left) and extension (right) of the lumbar spine

Exercise 13

AREAS STRETCHED: Buttocks and piriformis muscle
STARTING POSITION: Start lying on your back. Flex both knees and hips to 90°. Place the outside of the right ankle above the left knee.
TECHNIQUE: Use the left knee to pull the right ankle towards you, and at the same time use your right hand to press the right knee down towards your feet.
VARIATIONS: Altering the angle of flexion at the right hip will change the muscular emphasis of the exercise.
Points to note: This exercise combines external rotation with flexion of the right hip, and stretches the piriformis muscle deep in the pelvis. This muscle is sometimes associated with pain in the back and leg, by placing stress on the sciatic nerve. If you are unable to flex the left hip to 90° you may find your back begins to arch. Tighten your abdominals to prevent this.

Piriformis stretch

Exercise 14

AREAS STRETCHED: Anterior tibials, toe extensors, ankle joint
STARTING POSITION: Kneeling on all fours in bare feet, foot plantarflexed.
TECHNIQUE: Sit back on to your heels, taking some of your body-weight on your arms. Press the top (dorsum) of your foot to the ground.
VARIATIONS: Place a folded towel beneath your toe joints to increase the stretch on the toe extensors.
Points to note: The anterior tibials and toe extensors tend to be neglected in stretching. When tight, these muscles can give rise to 'shin splints', especially in those who exercise on hard surfaces or use road running as part of their fitness programme.

Anterior tibial stretch

Exercise 15

AREAS STRETCHED: Rectus femoris, iliopsoas

STARTING POSITION: Stand facing a wall with your left hand on the wall for support. Bend your right knee and grasp your right ankle.

TECHNIQUE: Pull your leg backwards from the hip, keeping your trunk upright.

PARTNER STRETCH: An assistant may tap the athlete's abdominal muscles to encourage the maintenance of muscle contraction, thus stabilising the lumbar spine and avoiding pelvic tilting.

VARIATIONS: Increasing the amount of knee flexion will increase the stretch on the lower portion of the rectus. Reducing the knee flexion but increasing hip extension will increase the stretch on the upper aspect of the muscle. If you are unable to grasp your ankle without bending your back, loop a towel around your foot and hold this instead.

Points to note: When the hip flexors are stretched they will tilt the pelvis forwards and increase the lumbar curve. To avoid this, tighten the abdominal muscles before applying the stretch, and keep them tight throughout the movement. Do not allow the knee to drift out to the side.

Rectus femoris stretch

Exercise 16

AREAS STRETCHED: Hamstrings

STARTING POSITION: Start lying on your back with your right knee pulled up towards your chest. Clasp your hands behind your knee, and keep your arms straight.

TECHNIQUE: Keeping your upper leg still, straighten your leg using the power of your quadriceps muscles alone.

PARTNER STRETCH: An assistant may grip the leg (without pressing directly over the patella) and apply the stretching force while keeping the knee locked.

VARIATIONS: If you are unable to reach behind your knee comfortably, loop a towel around your leg instead. Pulling your toes towards you will increase the stretch on the gastrocnemius muscles. Rotating the hip will change the muscle emphasis to the inner and outer hamstrings.

Points to note: This exercise uses the quadriceps contraction to provide the stretch on the hamstrings. By doing so the hamstrings are encouraged to relax through reciprocal innervation (see page 27). This stretch will also tighten the sciatic nerve. If you lift your head up or bend your back you may feel pins and needles in your leg.

Active hamstring stretch

Exercise 17

AREAS STRETCHED: Foot evertors, lateral ligament and the ankle

STARTING POSITION: Begin seated, with your right leg crossed over your left at ankle level. Grip beneath and to the outside of your right foot with your left hand. Stabilise your shin with your right hand.

TECHNIQUE: Keeping the shin still, pull your foot downwards (plantarflexion) and inwards (inversion) so you can see more of the sole of your foot.

VARIATIONS: Changing the angle of plantarflexion will alter the emphasis of the stretch.

Points to note: After you have sprained your ankle, the lateral ligament and the foot evertors will be tight. This exercise is especially good for regaining the lost flexibility and making the ankle more comfortable.

Foot evertor stretch

Exercise 18

AREAS STRETCHED: Plantarfascia, toe flexors

STARTING POSITION: Start in a lunge position with your right foot back. Roll on to the ball of your right foot and bend your right knee.

TECHNIQUE: Keep your toes flat and press your knee to the ground, increasing the flexion of your big-toe joint.

VARIATIONS: Straightening the leg and pressing it behind you will increase the stretch on the toe flexors. The movement is then similar to exercise 5, except the heel is lifted to transfer the stretch from the calf to the deep toe flexors.

Points to note: The plantarfascia can become tight as a result of everyday activities. If you then participate in your sport in bare feet, the toe joints may need to be more flexible.

Plantarfascia stretch

Exercise 19

AREAS STRETCHED: Thoracic spine and latissimus dorsi
STARTING POSITION: Hold on to a post with straight arms, then squat down.
TECHNIQUE: Lean back to exert a pull on the arms.
PARTNER STRETCH: This stretch may be performed in pairs as a tug-of-war, with both partners holding hands or holding a towel between them.
VARIATIONS: Holding the arms further apart reduces the abduction and stretches the latissimus less. Allowing the arms to bend and pressing the chest to the ground increases the stretch on the thoracic spine.
Points to note: The latissimus can become very tight in body-builders, while the thoracic spine is often tight in those who spend time leaning over a desk.

Thoracic spine stretch

Exercise 20

AREAS STRETCHED: Adductors excluding gracilus, buttocks

STARTING POSITION: Start standing with your feet wide apart and turned out towards the horizontal. Place your hands on your thighs.

TECHNIQUE: Squat down, pressing the knees apart and taking some of the body-weight through the arms on to the thighs.

VARIATIONS: Altering the angle of the feet will change the muscular emphasis of the exercise.

Points to note: Because the feet are turned out, the exercise position is quite unstable. If you feel yourself wobbling you can place one hand on a table to aid stability. Stress is placed on the inner (medial) knee ligaments, so those with knee pain should avoid this movement.

Short adductor stretch

Exercise 21

AREAS STRETCHED: Hamstrings

STARTING POSITION: Lie at the angle of a wall with your left leg beside it and your right leg on it. Your buttocks should be as close to the wall as possible.

TECHNIQUE: Press the back of your knee to the wall and at the same time slide your heel up the wall.

VARIATIONS: This is a particularly safe way in which to stretch the hamstrings, because the back is supported and the other leg holds the pelvis still. Those with tight hamstrings who have suffered back-pain will find this exercise particularly useful.

Hamstring stretch against wall

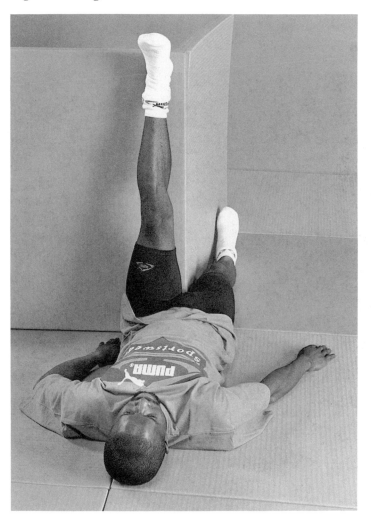

Exercise 22

AREAS STRETCHED: Hamstrings and buttocks of right leg, hip flexors of left leg

STARTING POSITION: Start kneeling down with your left knee on a cushion. Take your body-weight on your hands. Straighten your right leg and slide your left knee backwards into extension.

TECHNIQUE: Lower your body-weight, pressing your groin towards the ground.

VARIATIONS: Take your body-weight through two low stools placed at the side of the body.

Points to note: This is an advanced exercise. You must take time to ensure that you are stable and 'encourage', rather than force, the movement.

Supported splits position

Exercise 23

AREAS STRETCHED: Posterior neck structures

STARTING POSITION: Start sitting up straight in a chair with your back supported.

TECHNIQUE: Keep looking straight ahead. Tuck your chin in, pulling against it with your hands.

VARIATIONS: Place a towel behind your neck, positioned quite high up. Pull your chin back again, this time preventing any backwards movement of the neck with the towel.

Points to note: The movement should be purely horizontal, with no neck flexion or extension. Fix your eyes on an object directly in front of you to help maintain the correct alignment. People who spend a lot of time sitting in front of a VDU screen often have a faulty posture in which the neck is pulled forwards due to tight posterior neck structures: this head position can give rise to tension headaches. Stretching the posterior structures with this exercise can help to alleviate this problem.

Chin tuck

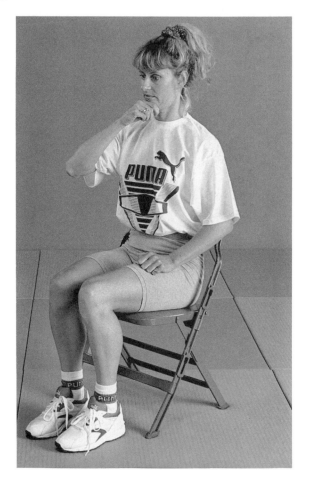

Exercise 24

AREAS STRETCHED: Lateral flexors of the neck

STARTING POSITION: Begin sitting upright in a chair with your spine supported. Grasp the side of the chair with your right hand to hold the shoulder down. Reach over your head with your left hand and take hold of the right side of your head.

TECHNIQUE: Pull your neck to the left using pressure from your left hand.

VARIATIONS: Rotating the head will change the muscular emphasis of the exercise.

Points to note: The exercise must begin from a position of good spinal alignment. Starting in a slumped sitting posture will increase the stress on the neck joints. Allowing the right shoulder to raise will reduce the stretch.

Neck side bend

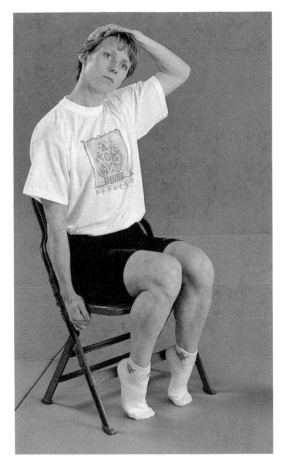

Exercise 25

AREAS STRETCHED: Pectorals, anterior deltoids

STARTING POSITION: Stand in a doorway in a lunge position with your arms raised and your forearms supported on the door-frame and wall.

TECHNIQUE   Lunge forwards, pressing the chest forwards and down.

VARIATIONS: Raising or lowering the starting position of the arms will change the muscular emphasis of the exercise.

Points to note: In a round-shouldered person the pectoral muscles are often very tight. This exercise, combined with strengthening exercises for the shoulder retractors (pulling muscles), will often correct the problem.

Chest stretch in doorway

Exercise 26

AREAS STRETCHED: Shoulder rotators

STARTING POSITION: Start standing up with your right arm reaching behind your neck and your left behind the small of your back.

TECHNIQUE: Pull your hands towards each other until they are as close as possible.

VARIATIONS: If you are unable to touch your fingertips together, grip a towel between your hands until your flexibility improves.

Points to note: It is usual for one arm to be less flexible than the other in this exercise.

Shoulder rotation stretch

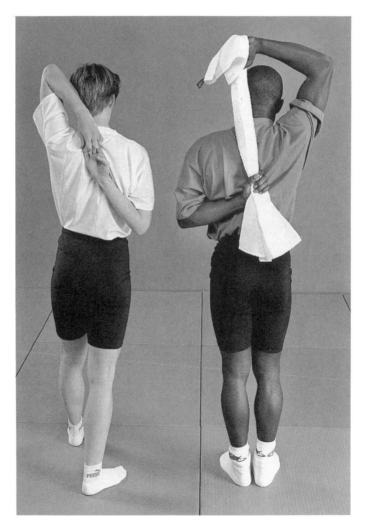

Exercise 27

AREAS STRETCHED: Pectorals, anterior deltoids, lateral rotators of the shoulder

STARTING POSITION: Begin sitting on the floor with your knees bent. Place your arms behind you with your hands together. Keep your arms straight.

TECHNIQUE: Lift your hips off the floor and press forwards with your knees, keeping your hands in the same place.

VARIATIONS: From the same starting position, instead of lifting the hips lift your hands backwards, keeping your arms straight and your hands together. Do not bend the trunk forwards.

Points to note: If your body-weight places too much stress on your shoulders, perform the exercise single handed (taking some of your weight on the other hand).

Anterior shoulder stretch

Exercise 28

AREAS STRETCHED: Wrist extensors and flexors
STARTING POSITION: Stand with your elbows out and the backs of your hands in contact.
TECHNIQUE: Keeping your elbows down, press the backs of your hands tightly together.
VARIATIONS: Pushing the arms forwards and pulling them back will change the muscular emphasis of the exercise. Placing the palms together will stretch the forearm flexors.
Points to note: These movements can be limited as a result of a wrist injury that has caused a lot of swelling. This is most noticeable if you compare the height of the right and left elbows.

Wrist flexor and extensor stretching

Exercise 29

AREAS STRETCHED: Pectorals, anterior deltoids, internal shoulder rotators

STARTING POSITION: Start in standing holding a stick above your head.

TECHNIQUE: Keeping the stick back, lower your arms in an attempt to place the stick behind your neck.

PARTNER STRETCH: Perform the stretch from a sitting position on the floor. An assistant stands behind the athlete, with his foot at the athlete's sacrum and the side of his leg along the length of the athlete's spine. A towel may be used as padding between the leg and spine. The assistant grips the stick and applies the stretching force. His leg keeps the athlete's spine straight and prevents the athlete from leaning back.

VARIATIONS: Placing the hands further apart or closer together will change the emphasis of the exercise. Holding the stick behind the small of the back and pulling it further backwards will stretch the external shoulder rotators.

Points to note: Keep looking forwards; do not flex your neck.

Shoulder stretch

Exercise 30

AREAS STRETCHED: Triceps

STARTING POSITION: Start in standing with your right hand behind your right shoulder blade, elbow pointing towards the ceiling.

TECHNIQUE: Cup your right elbow in your left hand and pull your right arm backwards, keeping it close in to your head.

VARIATIONS: Stretch both arms together, trying to reach your hands between your shoulder blades.

Points to note: Straightening the arm releases some of the stretch on the muscle.

Triceps stretch

Exercise 31

AREAS STRETCHED: Rectus femoris

STARTING POSITION: Lie on your left side with your left leg bent up. Hold your left knee with your left hand. Bend your right knee and hold your right ankle with your right hand.

TECHNIQUE: Pull the whole leg backwards, maintaining knee flexion.

PARTNER STRETCH: The athlete lies on a table with an assistant at his side. The athlete holds his left knee with both hands to fix his pelvis. The stretch on the right leg is applied by the assistant alone.

VARIATIONS: Loop a towel around the ankle to reduce the knee flexion and emphasise the stretch to the upper portion of the muscle.

Points to note: Keep the knee down to avoid abducting the hip. Holding the left leg will help to prevent the pelvis from tipping forwards and arching the spine. If this starts to occur, tighten the abdominal muscles to maintain the position of the lumbar spine.

Rectus femoris stretch

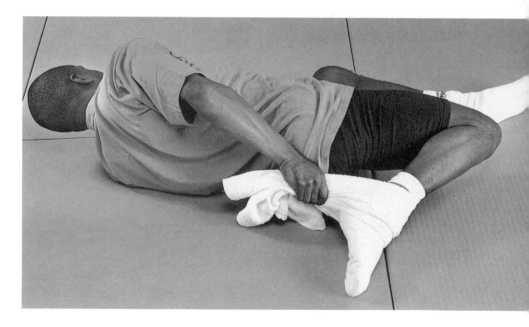

Exercise 32

AREAS STRETCHED: Buttock of the right leg, hip flexors of the left leg

STARTING POSITION: Begin by lying supine at the side of a bed or bench with your left leg over the bench side. Grasp your right leg behind the knee, keeping the knee flexed.

TECHNIQUE: Pull the right knee towards the chest.

VARIATIONS: Begin with the left heel on the bench; this will allow the right knee to be pulled up on to the chest completely because the lower spine will flex (*see* exercise 11). Hold this position and then lower the left leg over the side of the bench.

Points to note: The hip flexors are normally tighter than the hip extensors, so the lower leg gains the greater benefit from this exercise.

Hip flexor stretch (lying)

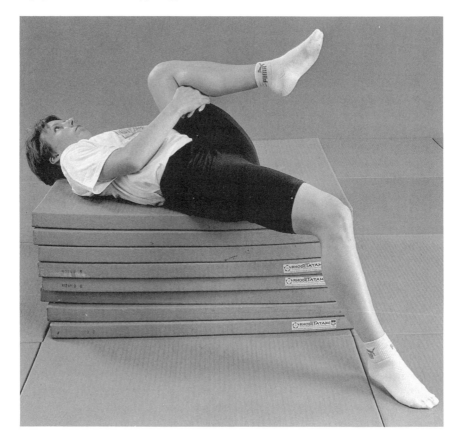

Exercise 33

AREAS STRETCHED: Hip flexors of left leg

STARTING POSITION: Begin in a half-kneeling position with your right leg forwards, foot flat on the floor. Rest your right arm on a stool to aid stability. Place your left hand on your left buttock.

TECHNIQUE: Tighten the abdominal muscles and lunge forwards, pressing with the left hand to force the left hip into extension.

VARIATIONS: Rotating the left hip so that the tibia lies at an angle to the sagittal plane will change the muscular emphasis of the exercise.

Points to note: Tightening the abdominals prevents the pelvis from tilting forwards. If the pelvis tilts, the spine will hyperextend and the range of motion will appear to increase, although the hip movement remains the same (see page 130).

Hip flexor stretch (half kneeling)

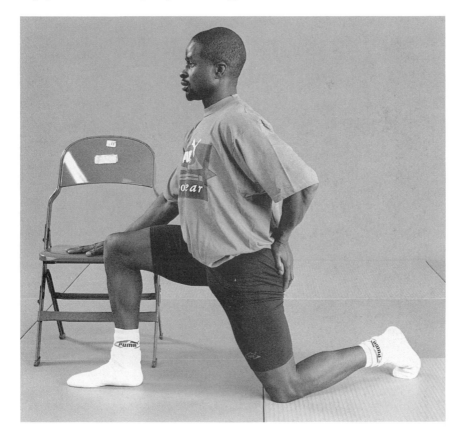

Exercise 34

AREAS STRETCHED: Spinal rotators, right hip abductors

STARTING POSITION: Start in 'long sitting'. Bend your right leg and cross it over the knee of your left at ankle level. Twist your trunk to the right and place your left elbow in front of your right knee. Pull your right arm back behind you.

TECHNIQUE: Increase the stretch on the spine and hip by pressing the left arm against the right knee and pulling the right arm further behind you.

VARIATIONS: Increasing the hip adduction of the right leg and reducing the twist of the spine will throw the emphasis on to the hip. Holding the hip still to prevent adduction will place the emphasis on the spine.

Points to note: If you find the starting position unstable, support yourself by placing your right hand on the floor.

Spinal rotation stretch

Exercise 35

AREAS STRETCHED: Posterior spinal structures

STARTING POSITION: Begin standing up with your right leg on a small stool. Place your hands on your right knee to take your body-weight.

TECHNIQUE: Flex the spine in an attempt to touch your head to your thigh. Take your body-weight through your hands on to your thighs.

VARIATIONS: Sit in a chair with one leg forwards, your hands supporting the weight of your body. Flex the spine as above.

Points to note: This exercise flexes the upper portions of the spine more than the lower (for the reverse see exercise 11). Normally these areas do not require stretching into flexion, but after injury resulting in prolonged rest they may stiffen.

Supported spinal flexion

Exercise 36

AREAS STRETCHED: Quadratus lumborum, obliques, latissimus dorsi

STARTING POSITION: Lie on your right side with two or three rolled pillows beneath you (above the hip). Slightly flex your left hip and allow your right leg to fall into adduction.

TECHNIQUE: Reach overhead with your left arm and 'sideflex' your trunk over the pillows in an attempt to touch your right shoulder to the floor.

Side flexor stretch

PARTNER STRETCH: An assistant kneels by your side and places one hand on your left hip and the other on your left shoulder. By leaning on to his hands and pressing his arms apart the assistant can increase the stretch.

VARIATIONS: Keeping your spine flat, extend your left leg at the hip and then adduct it to stretch the ilio tibial band (ITB).

Points to note: Adducting the right leg tips the pelvis and increases the emphasis on the lower portion of the body.

Side flexor stretch with arm as overpressure

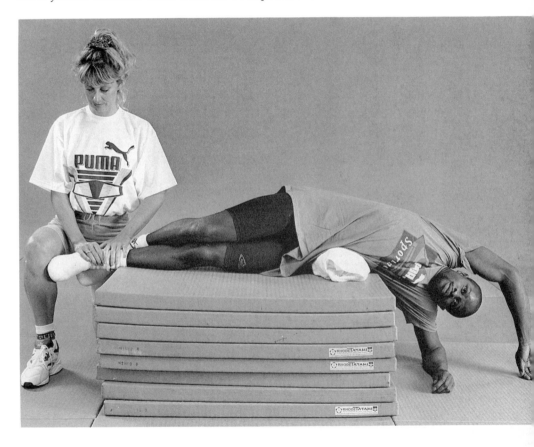

Exercise 37

AREAS STRETCHED: Spine and hip abductors

STARTING POSITION: Begin lying on your front with your arms up, and with the backs of your hands beneath your forehead.

TECHNIQUE: Lift your right leg upwards and cross it over your left, allowing your right knee to bend. As you do this, the right hip and right side of the chest should lift from the floor, but the shoulders and elbows stay down.

PARTNER STRETCH: An assistant kneels to your left and uses his left hand to hold your right shoulder in contact with the ground. The assistant's right hand places additional pressure on your right leg to increase the stretch.

VARIATIONS: As the knee flexion increases, the range of spinal rotation will increase. Reaching with the foot on the floor further over to the left will increase the stretch.

Points to note: This exercise combines rotation, lateral flexion and extension of the spine, and therefore opens the facet joints differently from exercise 10 which combines rotation, lateral flexion and flexion.

Prone spinal rotation

Exercise 38

AREAS STRETCHED: Spine, abdomen, and shoulder adductors
STARTING POSITION: Begin by sitting on the floor with your knees bent (crook sitting). Place the foot of the right knee on the front of the left thigh. The left foot rests on the outside of the left leg, so that the left hip is medially rotated and the right is laterally rotated. Place your right hand on the floor behind you, and your left hand overhead.
TECHNIQUE: Lift and press the hips forwards and to the right, allowing the left hip to lead the movement. Laterally flex and rotate your spine to the right. Your body-weight is taken on both knees and on the right hand, to form a 'tripod'.
PARTNER STRETCH: An assistant kneels behind you and presses your hips forwards and to the right to increase the stretch.
VARIATIONS: By altering the position of the right arm, either rotation or lateral flexion of the spine may be emphasised.
Points to note: Perform the exercise on a mat to cushion the knees. If the wrist of your right hand is painful as it takes your weight, press on your closed fist instead.

Combined rotation and lateral flexion stretch of the spine

Exercise 39

AREAS STRETCHED: Lateral fibres of deltoid, interscapular muscles. Joints at both ends of the clavicle

STARTING POSITION: Standing, with your right arm reaching across your body and your right hand over your left shoulder. The left hand cups the right elbow.

TECHNIQUE: By pulling with your left hand, press your right arm closer to your body and your right hand further over your left shoulder.

VARIATIONS: Reaching the right hand beneath the left arm rather than over the left shoulder will change the emphasis of the stretch.

Points to note: This stretch should not be performed if you have injured your acromioclavicular or sternoclavicular joints.

Shoulder stretch

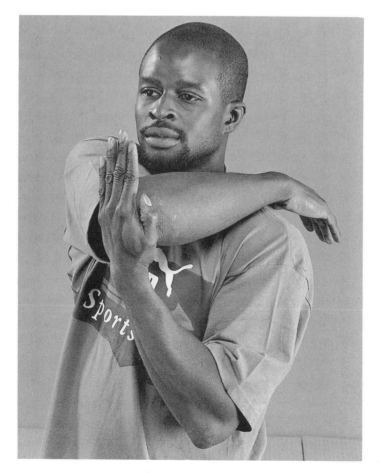

Exercise 40

AREAS STRETCHED: Adductors

STARTING POSITION: Sit on the floor with your feet astride. An assistant sits in front of you with the soles of his bare feet just above the insides of your knees. The assistant's knees are bent, and you both link arms together.

TECHNIQUE: The assistant's upper body stays still as you pull yourself forwards, keeping your spine straight. The assistant gently straightens his legs to press your hips further into abduction.

VARIATIONS: Place your hands on the floor behind you (see exercise 3) to support your spine while the assistant applies the abduction force with his legs as above.

Points to note: The assistant must be in bare feet for your comfort, and must apply the stretching force above the knees (to avoid placing stress on the medial ligament of the knees).

Partner stretch for hip adductors

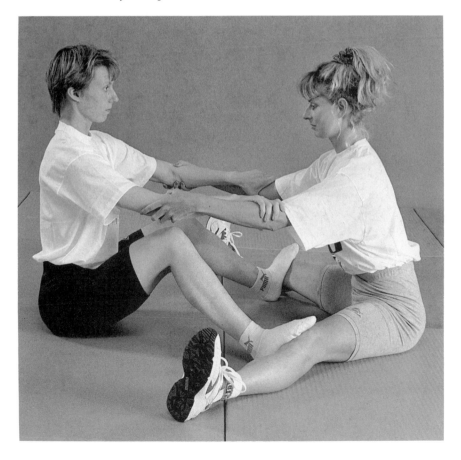

Exercise 41

AREAS STRETCHED: Hamstrings

STARTING POSITION: Begin with your back to a wall. An assistant stands in front of you with his knees bent and his feet apart. He places one bare foot on top of your left foot to stop it slipping. Place your right leg on the assistant's left shoulder and place your right hand on his left shoulder for stability. The assistant grips your leg above and below your knee to keep it locked.

TECHNIQUE: The assistant begins to stand up, thus raising the level of his shoulder and imparting the stretching force.

VARIATIONS: If you are very flexible the assistant will have to press your leg up away from his shoulder with his hands around your ankle.

Points to note: Stability is the key component of this exercise. The wall will stop you leaning back, and your foot is prevented from slipping by the assistant's foot. Your hand on the assistant's shoulder aids your stability.

Partner stretch for hamstrings

Exercise 42

AREAS STRETCHED: Pectorals and anterior deltoids
STARTING POSITION: Begin sitting on the floor with your knees bent. Bend your arms and place the backs of your hands on your forehead. An assistant stands behind you with his foot at your sacrum and the side of his knee along the length of your spine. A towel may be used as padding between the two areas. The assistant holds your elbows in his cupped hands.
TECHNIQUE: The assistant gently pulls your elbows back and upwards to impart the stretching force. Your spine is kept straight and prevented from moving by the pressure of the assistant's leg.
VARIATIONS: Place your hands behind you in the small of your back. The assistant pulls directly back on your elbows.
Points to note: These stretches should not be performed by anyone who has a history of shoulder dislocation.

Arm position for shoulder stretches

Exercise 43

AREAS STRETCHED: Rectus femoris

STARTING POSITION: Lie on a table with an assistant on your left side. Bend your right knee. The assistant grips around your right shin and beneath your right knee with his right arm. He presses down on your upper buttock with his left forearm to fix your pelvis.

TECHNIQUE: The assistant leans on to his left forearm to stabilise your pelvis, at the same time lifting your right hip into extension and pressing your right knee into flexion.

VARIATIONS: The leg may be lifted into extension first, and a block placed beneath the lower thigh to maintain the extended hip position. Knee flexion is now performed as the only movement.

Points to note: True hip extension must occur. If the pelvis tips forwards, the knee will lift from the table without the hip extending (see page 130).

Rectus femoris stretch with partner

Exercise 44

AREAS STRETCHED: Hip adductors

STARTING POSITION: Begin side-on to a wall with your right arm supported on the wall. An assistant stands behind and to the left of you, with his feet apart and his knees bent. His right foot is at the side of your right foot. Lift your left leg into abduction so the assistant can take hold of it, gripping above and below the knee.

TECHNIQUE: The assistant straightens his legs and lifts your leg further into abduction to impart the stretch.

VARIATIONS: If you are very flexible the assistant may need to grip your ankle.

Points to note: Stability is the key to this exercise. Your right foot is prevented from slipping by the pressure of the assistant's foot. The assistant must maintain a wide base of support. Pure abduction without hip flexion should occur.

Partner stretch for hip adductors

Exercise 45

AREAS STRETCHED: Shoulder elevators

STARTING POSITION: Sit on the floor with an assistant positioned behind you. The assistant places his hands over your shoulders.

TECHNIQUE: The assistant presses down on your shoulders to depress them.

VARIATIONS: The movement may be combined with neck lateral flexion and performed for one shoulder (for example, pressing down on the right shoulder and laterally flexing the neck to the left).

Points to note: As your assistant presses down, make sure you do not flex your spine or round your shoulders.

Passive shoulder depression

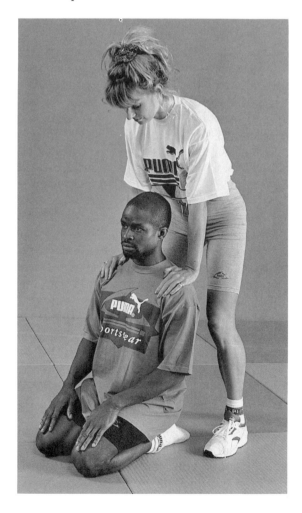

CHAPTER 8

Measuring flexibility

Flexibility should be measured in order to determine your existing range of motion, assess any muscle imbalance, and chart your progress as you train. When a muscle is more flexible than normal (hyperflexible) there is no need to stretch it. Indeed, to do so could leave you open to injury. If too much flexibility exists there may not be enough strength in the muscles supporting the joint to control the total range of motion: in such a case we say that hyperflexibility (greater than normal range of motion) has developed into instability (inability to control joint alignment through the whole available range).

You will also need to assess the ratio of muscle flexibility on one side of the joint to that on the opposing side. When there is a marked difference in flexibility or strength between the two, muscle imbalance is present (see page 38) and it would be wrong to practise an overall stretching programme. This would simply allow the imbalance to continue, although your muscles in general would be more flexible. When imbalance is detected the answer is to stretch only those muscles which are tight, and to strengthen those which are too loose (flabby) and weak, by exercising in the shortened (inner-range) position. Once the imbalance has been corrected a general flexibility programme may be used.

Stretching is a long-term part of any training programme, so you will need 'goals' or targets to aim at. For this you will need to measure your flexibility and aim at improving in a certain time. For example, you might aim at improving the range of motion of a joint by a certain number of degrees in a certain number of months, or to be able to reach far enough to touch a certain point by a set date (Christmas or birthdays, for instance). Either way, the goals you set yourself must be specific and realistic. In other words it is no good simply saying that you

121

want to increase your flexibility, because this is too open ended. Increase by how much, and in how long? Your goals must also be realistic: you may never be able to perform the splits if you are over 50 and very inflexible in the hip adductors. This really does not matter, provided that your degree of flexibility is appropriate to your age, body make-up and activity level. Remember, the right amount of stretching is the right amount for you as an individual. There is no competition – no winners and no losers.

Using the score charts

Table 7 can be used to test your flexibility. Average values are quoted, but remember that they are for general guidance only. If you have a specific problem which limits your flexibility you should see your physiotherapist.

You should perform a warm-up before testing any movement, and wear warm clothing to keep your body warm while performing the tests. Make sure that you perform the same degree of warm-up each time you measure your flexibility. The exercises are either active or static stretches (see page 53) and as such should be performed slowly and held in the stretched position. There should be no bobbing or bouncing actions which will give a deceptively high score. Each exercise is described briefly in the table, and the page reference for the full exercise is given in brackets.

Clinical flexibility testing

The testing tables can only give a rough, but still very useful, guide to flexibility. Where more precise measurement is needed, *clinical testing* is used. This accurately measures the angle of the joint at the point of maximal stretch, and is called *goniometry*. A number of goniometers are available. The simplest is the universal goniometer (see fig. 34). This consists of a 180° or 360° protractor. It has a single axis and scale but two arms. One arm is held stationary, the axis of the goniometer is placed on the axis (centre) of the joint to be measured, and the two arms rest on the mid-lines of the bones either side of the joint. The joint angle obtained when stretching is read from the centre scale.

The gravity goniometer consists of a needle inside a fluid-filled container. The needle points downwards due to gravity and acts as a reference against which the joint range is measured. The goniometer is strapped on to the limb and a direct reading is achieved.

Table 7 Flexibility tests

Test		Poor	Average	Good
1.		knee further than 15cm from rib-cage	knee 10–15cm from rib-cage	knee to rib-cage
Keep your straight leg on the floor and pull your bent knee towards your chest.		SCORE		
2.		more than 15 cm from floor	15 cm from floor	less than 15cm from floor
Keep the soles of your feet together and press your knees downwards towards the floor.				
3.		more than 15 cm from toes	10–15cm from toes	touching toes
Keep the knees locked and reach forwards towards the toes.				
4.		above horizontal	horizontal	below horizontal
The lower leg is bent up to the chest and held still, the top leg lowers towards the ground.				
5.		more than 60°	60°	less than 60°
Stand 0.5m from a wall. Lean forwards, keeping the feet flat on the floor and the knees locked.				

Table 7 cont'd   Flexibility tests

Test	Poor	Average	Good
6. Keep the forehead and chest on the ground and lift the straight arms upwards.	less than 15 cm	15–20cm	more than 20 cm
	SCORE		
7. Reach behind the back to try to touch the fingers together.	fingers more than 15cm apart	fingers 10–15cm apart	fingers touching
8. Keep the arms straight and try to cross them over as far as possible.	cross at wrist	cross at elbow	cross at upperarm
9. Keep the foot flat on a stool and press the knee towards the wall.	more than 50°	40°–50°	less than 40°
10. Keep the knees together and bent to 90°. Allow the heels to drop outwards.	less than 70°	70°–90°	more than 90°

Table 7 cont'd Flexibility tests

Test	Poor	Average	Good
11. Lock the arms flat out and measure the distance between the pelvic crest and the floor .	more than 10cm	5–10cm	less than 5cm
	SCORE		
12. Keep the arms flat on the floor and twist the trunk to allow the knees to lower towards the floor.	more than 10cm	10cm	0cm
13. Keep the small of the back on the chair back and flex the spine (not the hips) maximally .	fingers to mid-shin	fingers to floor	flat hand to floor
14. Keep the feet flat and knees locked. Without leaning forwards or backwards reach down the side of the leg .	fingers above knee	fingers to knee	fingers below knee
15. Keep both legs straight and flex one hip as far as possible.	less than 90°	90°	more than 90°

Table 7 cont'd   Flexibility tests

Test	Poor	Average	Good
16. Abduct both legs while keeping the small of the back flat and the legs straight.	less than 90°	90°	more than 90°
	SCORE		
17. Keep the knees together, and flex one knee maximally.	knee further than 10cm from buttock	knee to 5–10cm from buttock	knee to buttock
18. Keep the knees and ankles together throughout the test, and slowly sit back on to the heels. Measure the distance between the top (dorsum) of the foot and the ground.	greater than 5cm	5cm	flat
TOTAL SCORE			

FLEXIBILITY TESTS
- Perform thorough warm-up before measuring your flexibility.
- Hold each stretched position for 3 seconds before measuring.
- Do not bounce into the movement.
- Average values will vary with body size and type.

Using the goniometer

Figure 34 shows the plan for a simple goniometer. Photocopy this, stick the copy on to a piece of firm card or plastic and cut out the shape. Fasten the two pieces together with a clip. The goniometer is now ready for use.

To take a reading, position point A over the centre of rotation of the joint. This is the point of the joint around which the movement appears to take place. Figure 35 shows the centres of rotation for some large joints. To maintain accuracy the arms

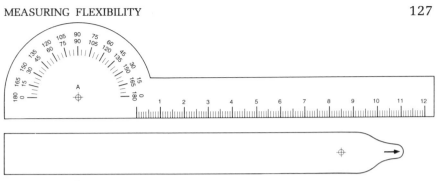

Fig. 34   The goniometer

of the goniometer must be positioned parallel to the bones, along
the mid-line of the limb. Figures 36(a) and 36(b) show correct
and incorrect alignment respectively. In figure 36(b) the upper
arm of the goniometer is not aligned along the mid-line of
the upper leg, so the reading obtained is lower, giving the
appearance of a less flexible joint.

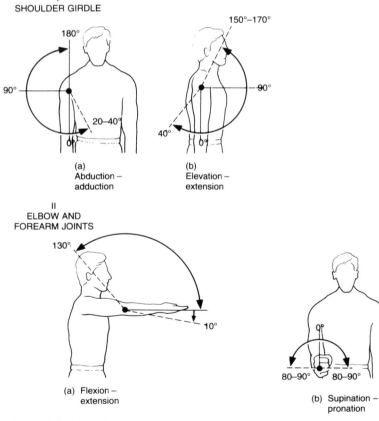

Fig. 35   Joint centres

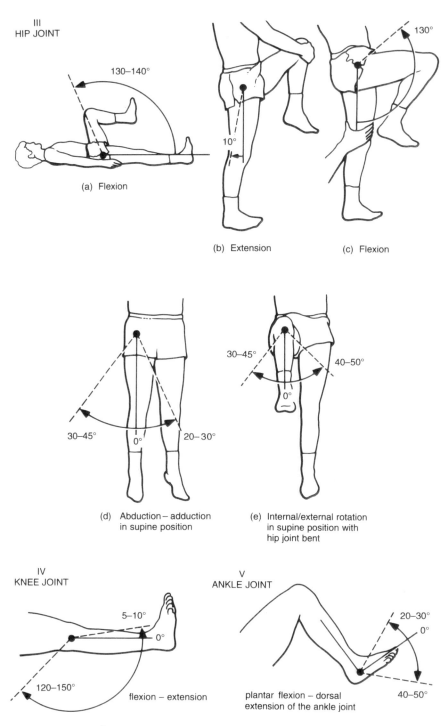

III
HIP JOINT

130–140°

10°

130°

(a) Flexion

(b) Extension   (c) Flexion

30–45°   0°   20–30°

30–45°   0°   40–50°

(d) Abduction – adduction
    in supine position

(e) Internal/external rotation
    in supine position with
    hip joint bent

IV
KNEE JOINT

V
ANKLE JOINT

5–10°   0°

20–30°   0°

120–150°   flexion – extension

plantar flexion – dorsal
extension of the ankle joint   40–50°

Fig. 35 cont'd   Joint centres

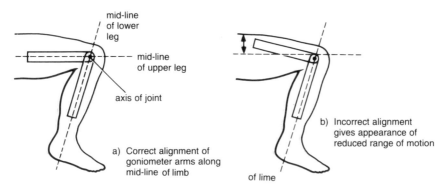

mid-line
of lower
leg

mid-line
of upper leg

axis of joint

b) Incorrect alignment
gives appearance of
reduced range of motion

a) Correct alignment of
goniometer arms along
mid-line of limb

of lime

Fig. 36   Correct goniometer positioning

What is being measured?

When the spine is moving in combination with either the lower
limb or upper limb, close examination is required to determine
which joints are actually taking part in the stretching exercise.
Tightness in the ligaments surrounding the hip means that once
the hip has flexed beyond 90° the pelvis starts to tilt and the
lower spine subsequently begins to flex. Total range of motion
may be made up of movements at a number of joints. In figure
37 the athlete appears to have long hamstrings because he is able
to touch his toes. In fact, the hamstrings are short and the pelvis

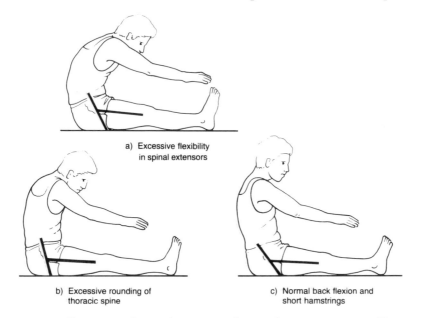

a) Excessive flexibility
in spinal extensors

b) Excessive rounding of
thoracic spine

c) Normal back flexion and
short hamstrings

Fig. 37   The sit-and-reach test – what is being measured?

has stayed tilted back. The movement is occurring in the lumbar spine because the subject's spinal extensors are excessively flexible. In figure 37(b) the hamstrings are the same length as those of subject 37(a), but the back extensors are of average length. Now, the total range of motion is considerably reduced. In figure 37(c) the range of motion appears great, but neither the hamstrings nor the spinal extensors are flexible. Instead the movement is coming from the thoracic spine which is rounding excessively.

Pelvic tilt is also an important factor in determining hip motion. In figures 38(a) and 38(b) the length of the rectus femoris is being measured (see page 89). In figure 38(a) no pelvic tilt is occurring and the range of hip extension is seen to be limited. In figure 38(b) the same range of hip extension is occurring, but the anterior tilt of the pelvis occuring at the same time gives an increase in total range of motion.

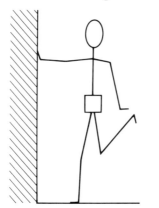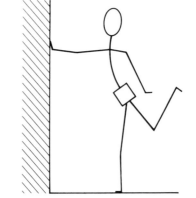

Fig. 38   Pelvic tilt and hip extension

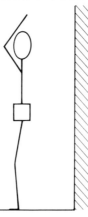

Fig. 39   Spine and shoulder movements

Movement of the spine with the shoulder is also important. In figures 39(a) and 39(b) the range of shoulder elevation is being measured against the wall. In figure 39(a) the movement is seen to be limited, but in figure 39(b) there appears to be a greater range of motion. In fact, the range of motion at the shoulder is exactly the same in each case; it is the movement occurring in the spine which is greater in the second figure.

When measuring joint movement it is essential to limit the motion to a single joint. This can be achieved by looking closely at the body and repeating the movement to ensure accuracy.

CHAPTER 9

Flexibility, sport and therapy

Tissue healing

If you slip on a pavement and sprain your ankle, the body reacts immediately by beginning a healing process. This process can be divided into three phases: *inflammation, proliferation,* and *remodelling.* Following injury the inflammatory phase lasts between four and six days. The appearance of the body at this time reveals four classic signs of inflammation. These are redness, heat, swelling and pain which together lead to a loss of function in the injured body-part (*see* fig. 40). When tissues tear, small blood vessels are ruptured releasing blood into the surrounding area. Injured tissue-cells die and chemicals are released which irritate the local tissues. There is an increase in the local blood flow which causes the red appearance.

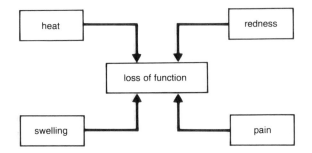

Fig. 40   *The signs of inflammation*

Changes in the concentration of fluids around the blood vessels cause watery fluid to leak out of the blood vessels and into the surrounding tissues, giving rise to swelling. If the injury is close to the body surface, for example to the ankle ligaments, the swelling is readily apparent. If the injury is deeper in, however, the swelling may not be seen on the body surface, only

132

felt as pressure and stiffness. The increased metabolic activity which the inflammation involves causes heat which is felt over the skin surface. The combination of pressure from the swelling and chemical irritation from metabolic products resulting from the inflammatory process causes pain.

With a minor injury the inflammatory stage may end in three days, but with more serious injuries inflammation can remain active for five or six days. During this time the strength of the injured tissues relies on clotted blood and tissue fluids and so the injured area is very weak. Any stretching applied at this stage can easily disrupt the healing process and prolong the inflammation. This will effectively make the total healing time much longer.

Following this, proliferation occurs. The cells within the area which was supplied by the damaged blood capillaries will have died. These must be removed if healing is to be effective. Removal of dead cells is the job of special blood cells which engulf the dead material and digest it. Once this has occurred, new capillaries start to grow into the damaged area, forming delicate granulation tissue. By the fifth day after injury a special form of tissue called *collagen* has started to form; this material will join the damaged tissues and form a bridge.

The collagen fibres are laid down haphazardly, and if this orientation remains the scar formed will be very weak. To improve the strength of the scar, gentle movement should be performed. This will stretch the healing collagen fibres and cause them to line up in the direction of stress, making the eventual scar far stronger.

Most of the collagen is laid down between 16 and 21 days after injury, so this is the time when stiffness will be greatest. It is therefore during this stage that stretching will be most effective.

Twenty-one days after the injury the remodelling phase begins. During this stage the amount of collagen produced is equal to the amount broken down. Although the total amount of collagen remains the same, the fibres will overlap and form a mat of adhesions which will stick to the surrounding tissues if movement is not performed. Also, the collagen will begin to shrink unless stretching exercises are continued.

Time-scale for stretching

It becomes clear from the effects of healing that stretching is not appropriate immediately after injury. There are two reasons for this. First, the injured area is very weak and easily disrupted.

Any amount of stretching could easily pull it and increase the tissue damage: this in turn will re-start the inflammation. Second, collagen tissue will not begin to form until the dead material produced by the injury has been removed, so until this happens there is really nothing there to stretch.

We can divide the post-injury period into two distinct phases (see fig. 41). The first is the *acute* phase, from the time of injury to five days later. During this time the area is still inflamed, and our aim should be to minimise the effects of the injury. This may be achieved by using ice or cold water to slow the metabolic rate and reduce cell death from the low amount of oxygen present in the area. Swelling should be contained by using an elasticated bandage. During this period the fitness of the rest of the body should be maintained by using exercises which do not stress the injured area. After five days the inflammation will have subsided, and we enter the *restoration* phase. Stretching is needed to ensure that the collagen fibres of the injured tissue become strong and face in the right direction to support the body-part. Strengthening exercises must also be performed to tense the muscles and broaden them. This has the effect of moving the muscle fibres apart and preventing them from sticking together.

RECOVERY FROM INJURY

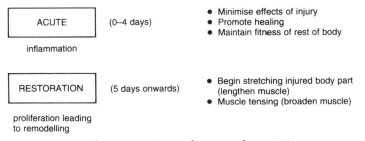

Fig. 41   *Acute and restoration phases of an injury*

Classification of injury

When muscles are injured we say they are *strained*; when ligaments are injured they are *sprained*. Both strains and sprains may be categorised in grades which represent the severity of the injury and the amount of tissue that has been damaged.

Three grades of ligament injuries are used. Grade I sprains involve only slight tissue damage and the area is tender to touch. Swelling is only slight, and the body-part moves almost normally. With the grade II sprain, more ligament fibres are injured. Local pain is more intense and movement is more limited. Grade I and II injuries are common when the ankle is twisted, for example. Grade III injuries are far more serious because they involve complete rupture of the tendon. A skiing injury is a typical example of this type. There is considerable pain and swelling, and it is impossible to take the body-weight through the injured limb. These injuries often require surgery to repair the ruptured ligament, followed by intensive physiotherapy.

Muscle strains may be classified in four levels. The grade I (mild) strain involves tearing of only a few muscle fibres and subsequent local bruising. The area feels stiff for a few days and then clears up fairly quickly. Grade II (moderate) strains are more severe. A larger number of muscle fibres are injured, and injury occurs over a greater area. The muscle membrane (fascia) still remains intact, so bleeding is contained within the muscle and forms what is called an *intramuscular haematoma*. The area again feels tight, but this time a local raised area is felt over the bruising. When tensed or stretched the muscle gives pain. A pulled hamstring is an example of a grade I or II muscle strain. With grade III (severe) strains a larger area of muscle is affected. The muscle fascia is partially torn, and more than one muscle may be involved. Bleeding is more profuse, and it spreads over a larger area. Because the muscle fascia has torn, blood spreads throughout the area causing skin discoloration. A typical example here is a 'dead leg', where bruising spreads from the injured thigh down into the knee and calf. The grade IV injury is a complete rupture. The muscle-ends contract and a definite gap can be felt between the injured muscle fibres. In some cases a snapping sound may have been heard at the time of injury. Bleeding and swelling are considerable, and the muscle cannot be tensed up. This type of injury may require hospital treatment.

The classification of injury is a guide to the period of rest and the amount of stretching that is required. As a general rule the stretching should not be painful, but you should feel that it is lengthening the muscle. Never force a stretch, and never exercise through increasing pain. If something is painful, and the pain goes away with stretching, that is fine. If the pain starts to increase, however, the stretch should be stopped.

The following stretches are for general guidance only. If you suffer a sports injury, see a physiotherapist. The sooner an injury is seen, the better. If left without treatment, injuries can put you out of sport for far longer. In addition, minor aches and pains are often signs that something is going wrong with the body. If this is caught in time a more severe injury can often be prevented.

The sprained ankle

When you sprain your ankle, the most common injury is to a
portion of the lateral ligament on the outside of the joint. This
tissue limits plantarflexion, inversion and adduction of the foot.
The easiest way to stretch this area out is to cross the injured leg
at the shin over the uninjured one. One hand steadies the lower
leg on the injured side, while the other is cupped around the foot
and ankle to pull it down, round and inwards. The stretch
should be gentle and static.

Once this has been achieved, the next stage is to stretch the
ankle actively by standing and rocking over on to the outer edge
of the foot, or by walking on an inclined surface. This movement
is controlled, but eventually faster actions must be used to
develop agility in the ankle structures. This can be achieved by
walking on an uneven surface such as soft ground or sand. You
can also make your own uneven surface by placing four or five
cushions on the ground and walking, and then slowly jogging,
over them in bare feet. At each stage the action must be
controlled so you don't feel that the movement is 'running away'
with you.

The pulled hamstring

When you tear a hamstring you may injure the muscle in its
centre part (belly) or at the musculo–tendinous (MT) junction –
the point at which the hamstring joins to the bones of the pelvis
or the knee via the muscle tendon (see fig. 42). The difference
between these two areas is that the MT junction does not
contract, while the muscle belly does. As well as stretching,
muscle-belly tears will need strength training to broaden the
muscle and separate the muscle fibres to prevent them from
sticking together. Injury to the MT junction often responds to
stretching alone.

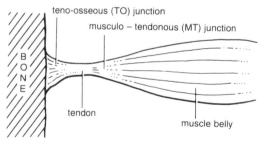

Fig. 42   Areas of injury in a muscle

Because the hamstrings work over the hip and the knee, two types of stretches must be done. First, the muscle must be stretched with the leg straight (see page 90). Once adequate flexibility has been regained the elastic strength of the muscle must be worked on. First stretch the muscle, then contract it rapidly from this lengthened position. To do this, lie face-down on a bench with the injured leg over the bench side so that the hip is flexed to 90°. A small (3 kg) weight is attached around the ankle. From the stretched position the hip is extended to pull the leg upwards against the resistance of the weight (see fig. 43(a)). The movement may be modified to use both the knee and the hip by training with a partner. The partner provides the resistance by pushing on the heel, and the movement starts with the knee and hip both flexed to 90°. From here, the action is to extend both the hip and knee simultaneously against resistance, hold the maximally contracted position for 1–2 seconds, and then lower the leg while maintaining tension in the muscle (see fig. 43(b)). This controlled action progresses to spring jumping actions (see fig. 43(c)), moving from a flexed hip/knee position to a fully extended position.

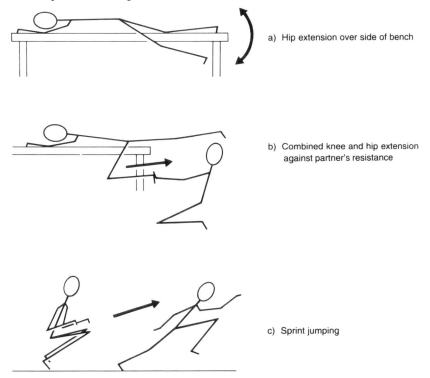

a) Hip extension over side of bench

b) Combined knee and hip extension
    against partner's resistance

c) Sprint jumping

Fig. 43   *Combining strength and stretch of the hamstrings*

The swollen knee

When the knee suffers a minor injury it will swell. This swelling limits the movement of the joint. As the swelling clots and the injury heals, both the physiological movements and the accessory movements of the joint will be limited (see page 24). This means that the joint will lose its normal movement and its healthy springy feeling (joint play). Stretching into flexion and extension will help you to regain the physiological movements, but the accessory movements will only return if these actions are combined with stresses to the knee which apply rotatory and shearing forces. This will work on all aspects of agility, and also help to build 'confidence' in the knee.

Start by standing with the feet shoulder-width apart, and step forwards and across with the uninjured leg so that the stress is taken on the injured knee. Step backwards and across to place the opposite stress on the joint (see fig. 44(a)). This action may be used as a side-step to perform a 'grapevine' action. Bending the knee further will increase the stress on the knee, and performing the action over a bench to bend the knee to near-maximum will test the knee fully (see fig. 44(b)). Because these actions stress the knee considerably they must be carefully controlled.

a) 'Grapevine' movement to place sideways stress on knee

b) Increasing range of movement

Fig. 44   Developing agility in the knee

Where the rotation movement of the knee is limited, particularly after injury to the inner ligament (medial collateral ligament), this can be regained by twisting the tibia on the femur. A simple exercise is to place the foot up on a swivel chair so that the knee and hip are flexed to 90°. Turn the chair by twisting the tibia and foot. As the foot moves outwards the tibia is externally rotated and the medial ligament is stretched. Gentle stretching of this type will make the ligament stronger by stressing and relaxing it to help the ligament fibres line up in the direction of the stress on the knee.

The 'kicking' muscle

Injury to the rectus femoris or the 'kicking muscle' is common in football. The injury usually occurs either when an ineffective warm-up has been performed, or towards the end of the game when fatigue sets in. Either way, stretching will be needed to restore the length and spring of the muscle. Passive stretching is performed by simultaneously flexing the knee and extending the hip (see page 89). Once the same range can be achieved on both the injured and the uninjured side, the elastic strength of the muscle must be worked on. The action is to move from this fully stretched position to a fully contracted position of hip flexion and knee extension. This is performed against a resistance which can be supplied by an elastic band, by a low pulley in a weight-training room, or by a training partner (see fig. 45).

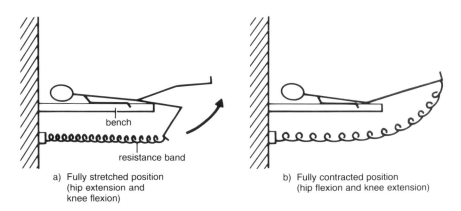

a) Fully stretched position
(hip extension and
knee flexion)

b) Fully contracted position
(hip flexion and knee extension)

Fig. 45   Stretch–contract of the rectus femoris

The dead leg

A 'dead leg' occurs when the quadriceps muscles of the thigh are severely bruised. This normally happens in rugby when a knee or head contacts the thigh at speed in a tackle. Blood vessels are ruptured and a large amount of blood is released into the muscle. The result is a large tense area within the muscle caused by a combination of blood and swelling. As the condition heals, the bruising tracks down through the muscle into the knee and calf. The athlete is unable to bend the knee because of tension in the quadriceps. The danger with this injury is that the release of blood can cause the area to calcify and form calcium bone salts within the muscle. If this happens it can be very serious, so stretching must be applied very cautiously under the supervision of a physiotherapist.

Initially, only active stretches should be used by lying prone and simply flexing the knee through the power of the hamstrings alone. Once 90° knee flexion has been obtained, very gentle passive stretches may begin by lying supine and pulling the heel up towards the buttock. A towel placed around the ankle makes the reach easier. When the range of movement increases further, and the pain and bruising subside, greater overpressure can be used to stretch the quadriceps by kneeling and sitting back on to the ankles.

The calf and Achilles

When the Achilles is injured, calf stretches are performed with the knee flexed (see page 79). When the calf is injured, it is usually the long gastrocnemius muscle which is affected. This muscle is stretched with the knee straight. When this can be performed statically without pain, an active stretch is used. Place the ball of the foot on a 5 cm block (a thick book). Allow the heel to lower down, keeping the knee locked: this will stretch the gastrocnemius. From this position raise up on to the toes against your body-weight.

Initially you should hold on to something to take some of your body-weight off the calf. Eventually, full body-weight may be used and the exercise can be speeded up until faster, more explosive actions are used to work the muscle for elastic strength.

The arch of the foot

In sports such as the martial arts and some types of dance, which are carried out in bare feet or in very thin shoes, the amount of motion available to the big-toe joint can overstretch one of the structures which forms the arch of the foot. This structure, the plantarfascia, can become inflamed or damaged. If this happens, stretching should be employed once the injury has healed in order to restore the flexibility of the plantarfascia. This can be achieved in a lunge position by plantarflexing the foot and flexing the toes simultaneously. Begin in a lunge position, lift the heel to plantarflex the foot, and then bend the knee (pressing it towards the floor to flex the big-toe joint – see page 92).

The ribs

The ribs may be bruised or cracked in a rugby tackle or when hit by the ball in hockey or cricket. When the injury has healed, stiffness often remains because the muscles between the ribs (intercostals) have tightened. To open the ribs and stretch the intercostals we need to combine overhead reaching actions with deep breathing. Twisting the trunk away from the painful area will increase the stretch still further. When performing this exercise be careful not to take too many deep breaths without a rest, because this could cause you to hyperventilate and become light-headed. Perform the exercise three times and then breathe normally for 30–60 seconds before trying again.

The frozen shoulder

When the shoulder is injured it will swell and the joint capsule will fill with fluid. This will cause the capsule to tighten, eventually limiting the movement of the whole joint. The shape of the capsule is such that certain movements will be limited more than others. In the case of the shoulder this means that lateral rotation (placing the hand behind the neck) becomes more limited and painful than medial rotation (putting the hand behind the back). The rotation movements may be regained by trying to touch the fingers together behind the back (see page 100). In addition, the joint play may be regained by holding on to an object and leaning back to pull the shoulder along its length and apply traction (*see* fig. 46(a)). Alternatively, sit sideways on a dining chair and hang your arm over the chair back. Place a thick towel over the chair back to pad the armpit area. Grasp something in the hand to provide a traction force, and pull down on the stiff arm with the other arm to give overpressure (*see* fig. 46(b)).

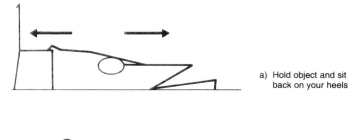

a) Hold object and sit back on your heels

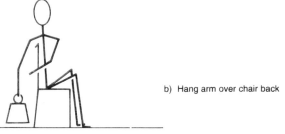

b) Hang arm over chair back

Fig. 46   *Self-traction in the shoulder joint*

Tennis elbow

In tennis elbow the muscle most commonly affected is one which extends the wrist (extensor carpi radialis longus). This muscle will become tight, and must be stretched by flexing the wrist while keeping the elbow locked out. If the elbow is allowed to bend even slightly the stretch will be taken off. A simple exercise is to stand facing a wall, and to straighten the elbow and keep it locked with pressure from the other hand. Place the back of the hand on the injured side against the wall and lean forwards to press the wrist into flexion. Performed correctly, this stretch can be felt up the whole arm and into the elbow.

Wrist injury

Following a wrist injury such as a severe sprain or fracture, most of the movements at the wrist will be limited. To regain these, three exercises are important. The first two are performed with the hand flat on a table top. Initially the hand is placed palm down on the table surface, with the wrist crease at the table edge. The uninjured hand is placed on top of the injured one, and the elbow is moved up and down to produce flexion and extension of the wrist (see fig. 47(a)). The leverage provided by the forearm combined with the weight of the body provides overpressure at end-range for the static stretch.

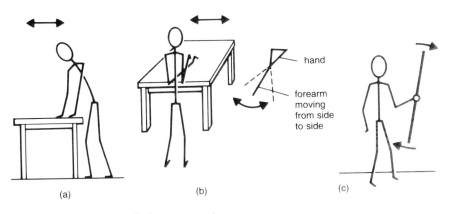

hand

forearm moving from side to side

(a)   (b)   (c)

Fig. 47   Wrist mobility exercises

For the second exercise the hand is moved into the centre of the table, so that the whole forearm is supported, and again the uninjured hand holds the injured one flat against the table surface. The elbow on the injured side is moved from side to side, sliding over the table surface to perform abduction and adduction of the injured wrist (see fig. 47(b)). Finally, the arm is held at 90° flexion with the elbow close into the side of the body, the injured forearm supported by the cupped uninjured hand. A stick is held in the hand, and pronation and supination performed. Aim to move the stick into a horizontal position (see fig. 47(c)).

CHAPTER 10

Sport-specific stretching

In the majority of sports there is a central core of muscles which require stretching. Most sports involve some type of running action: this may be repeated running (marathon); single step running or lunging (badminton); or small bursts of speed (football). In each case the muscles used are similar, but the intensity of use and the range of motion through which the muscles are put will differ. While the running action forms the basis of motion, the throwing action is frequently involved either with a ball (throw and catch) or with an implement used to strike an object (racquet or bat).

Superimposed on these basic sports movements are actions specific to the individual sports themselves. For example, the double-arm throwing action used in football differs considerably from the action of throwing the javelin, while the striking action of bat on ball in cricket is different from that of hitting a ball with a tennis racquet.

To build up a comprehensive stretching programme for sports, then, we need to choose exercises which cover both the central core and the specific skills. By analysing which muscles are used in an action we can estimate the patterns of muscle tightness which are likely to occur for each sport. Developing a stretching programme in this way can achieve two things. First, sports actions will be more efficient because we maintain a high range of motion. As we have seen on page 33, when a muscle is contracted from a comfortably stretched position the amount of force achieved is greater than if a muscle is contracted from a shortened position. By stretching we are therefore enhancing sports performance. Second, by preventing excessive shortening in general, and muscle imbalance in particular, we are maintaining optimal joint alignment. This provides a foundation for good biomechanics and balanced joint loading, increasing the likelihood of injury prevention.

Movement analysis of core sports actions

Running

Running differs from walking in that when we walk we have at least one foot on the ground at all times. When we run we literally jump from foot to foot, so there is a stage when both feet are off the ground and the body is airborne. For this reason, running may be divided into two component phases, *stance* and *swing*. In the stance phase the foot is on the ground, and the body is decelerating. The muscles are working eccentrically to slow the body down and absorb shock through the whole of the lower limb. At the moment when the foot strikes the ground, the body-weight is taken through the heel. As the body-weight moves forwards the foot flattens to absorb the shock, and finally the foot pushes with the toes to accelerate the body once more and propel it forwards. The forward action signals the start of the swing phase when the foot is off the ground. The limb is now accelerating and being catapulted through the air.

During heel strike, the anterior tibial muscles work to stop the foot slapping down on the ground, while the posterior tibials stop the foot from flattening too much. Tightness of either of these two muscle groups can be a cause of shin pain in runners. In mid-stance the knee is bent slightly and the quadriceps work to provide the spring in the legs, while the hip abductors support the pelvis and prevent it dipping down at the side. Tightness in these muscles at this stage of running is one cause of pain at the side of the leg and knee (or 'runner's knee'). As the heel rises and we begin to push off from the floor, the hamstrings rapidly extend the hip while the calf muscles plantarflex the foot. Both provide the thrust in running. If either muscle is tight it is more likely to tear during sudden lunging or sprinting actions.

During the swing phase, the hip flexors lift the leg through. These may become tight and therefore more susceptible to injury, but more usually any excessive tightness or shortness will affect the lumbar spine.

Sports involving the running action will require calf, Achilles and anterior tibial stretches. In addition the hip flexors, hamstrings and quadriceps should be stretched together with the adductors. Sprinting actions will require more attention to the hamstrings, while kicking actions will need stretching for the rectus femoris. Endurance running will need stretching for the ilio tibial band (ITB) and anterior tibial muscles in particular to protect against overuse friction injuries to these areas.

Throwing

In many sports the throwing mechanism is very similar. A javelin throw and an overhead shot in tennis may seem very different, but both have three phases. Initially there is the *cocking* phase, in which the arm is held up and back in preparation for the strike. The shoulder is abducted and externally rotated, the elbow flexed, and the wrist extended. This position stretches the anterior shoulder structures and the shoulder rotators and can place considerable stress on the medial ligament of the elbow. As the arm is pulled forwards into the striking position, it enters the *acceleration* phase. The body and shoulder lead the movement, coming forwards and leaving the arm behind, pre-stretching the shoulder tissues. The shoulder flexors then rapidly contract with the shoulder rotators and elbow extensors to simultaneously bring the arm forwards and in. The acceleration phase takes place as a whipping action and so places considerable stress on the elbow structures. As the hand is flung forwards the arm enters its final phase, the *follow-through*. The object being thrown is released from the hand, and the elbow extends rapidly. This places considerable stress on the bony knuckle of the ulna (olecranon process) as the elbow locks out.

Sports involving any type of throwing action will require stretches to the anterior shoulder structures, the shoulder rotators and the elbow flexors. In addition, because of the single-arm nature of throwing, stretching must ensure symmetry between the two upper limbs.

Sport-specific stretches

Once stretching has been practised for the core sports skills, specific stretches are required for individual sports. To decide which stretches to use we must analyse the major movements involved.

To analyse the movement used in a particular sport we need to look at which joints are moved, the range of movement that these joints are taken through, and the muscles involved in the movements. Clearly it is the muscles stretched by large movement ranges that we are concerned with, because these will be the ones needing stretching exercise. When throwing the javelin, for example, the shoulder and elbow of the throwing arm travel though extreme ranges and so will need stretching. The amount of use to which particular muscles are subjected must also be noted. Those used powerfully may be likely to shorten and require additional stretching. The pectorals and anterior deltoids are used powerfully when performing bench-press actions in weight training and so tend to become very short.

Postures used in a sport are also a clue to the stretches which may be needed. Prolonged activity in a particular posture will cause the body to adapt by lengthening muscles on over-stretched joints and shortening those over joints not moved through an adequate range. In cycling, for example, the stooped position of the thoracic spine can give rise to stiffness and pain in this area. Sport-specific stretches are detailed in table 8.

Table 8 Sport-specific stretching

Exercise	Running	Throwing	Racquet sports	Aerobics	Step	Martial arts	Swimming	Cricket	Weight training	Canoeing	Rock climbing	Windsurfing	Rugby	Football	Hockey	Netball and basketball	Skiing	Waterskiing	Baseball	American football	Horse riding	Table tennis	Cycling	Golf
1		✓							✓										✓	✓				
2																								
3											✓	✓			✓			✓		✓			✓	
4		✓													✓									
5		✓																						
6		✓	✓																	✓				
7			✓				✓				✓					✓						✓		
8																✓								
9																								
10	✓																							
11																								
12	✓																							
13																								
14																								
15				✓									✓											
16																	✓				✓			
17			✓		✓													✓					✓	
18																								
19	✓					✓																		
20	✓																							
21																								
22																								

Exercise	23	24	25	26	27	28	29	30	31	32	33	34	35	36	37	38	39	40	41	42	43	44	45
Running		✓	✓	✓						✓	✓												
Throwing							✓																✓
Racquet sports																							
Aerobics																✓							
Step								✓															
Martial arts																		✓	✓	✓			
Swimming																					✓		
Cricket											✓*												
Weight training				✓																			
Canoeing								✓		✓	✓												✓
Rock climbing																							
Windsurfing						✓																	
Rugby										✓			✓										
Football				✓	✓	✓																	
Hockey																							
Netball and basketball																							✓
Skiing	✓																						
Waterskiing				✓	✓																		
Baseball																							✓
American football																							
Horse riding			✓																				
Table tennis			✓			✓																	
Cycling							✓																
Golf										✓*													

Index